THE WORLD OF THE GRIZZLY BEAR

LIVING WORLD BOOKS
John K. Terres, Editor

The World of the
GRIZZLY BEAR

Text and Photographs by

W. J. Schoonmaker

J. B. LIPPINCOTT COMPANY
Philadelphia & New York

Respectfully dedicated to all of those who hunt with binoculars and cameras

Contents

Author's Introduction

No ONE MAN knows all there is to know about any species of animal, so experiences and observations recorded from early times to the present have been gleaned in order to make this book more complete.

The reputation of the grizzly bear has been based largely upon the tales of woodsmen who hunted the bear but did not study it and upon the opinions of biased cattlemen and settlers who never really knew the grizzly because they feared it. Reputation may be false and it often is.

In order to learn the true character of this big bear, I have relied upon studies and observations of naturalists and scientists. Records of the past have been added to knowledge recently acquired so we may have an accurate account of the grizzly from the past to the present.

To those who preceded us and left valuable tales and records we must be grateful. How else would we know of the California grizzly in the early 1800's and of the bears that dwelt in forests from which they have long since vanished?

The observations of different naturalists may be accurate yet not in agreement, because individual animals, including the grizzly, may not react in the same way in similar or identical situations.

W. J. Schoonmaker

Rensselaer, New York
September, 1967

Meet the Grizzly Bear

IF YOU EVER come face to face with a huge bear, almost bigger than you could imagine, it will surely be a grizzly because these are the largest carnivores, or flesh-eating mammals, in the world. If the gigantic beast were to stand up on its hind feet and look down at you from a height of nine feet, you would realize at once that by comparison, in size and strength, all men are insignificant.

True, the grizzly bear is not as heavy as the elephant, which may weigh six or seven tons, but the elephant is a plant-eater. Nor is the grizzly as big as the blue whale, which may reach a length of a hundred feet and

The grizzly bear is the largest carnivore, or flesh-eating mammal, in the world.

weigh up to 250,000 pounds and is, as far as we know, the largest animal that ever lived. Whales, however, are marine mammals, and the blue whale, despite its huge size, feeds chiefly upon tiny, shrimplike animals that swim about in the ocean in countless millions.

Most of us are apt to call all furry creatures "animals," but scientists classify them as mammals. As most of us know, every living thing is either a plant or an animal. A mammal is specifically an animal with a backbone, more or less covered with hair. It is warm-blooded, gives birth to living young, and suckles its offspring. Two mammals, however, are a striking exception in the way their young are born. The primitive duckbill and the spiny anteater, for example, lay eggs as do birds.

It has been estimated that there are about one million species of animals and that 3,500 of these are mammals. At least 1,500 species and subspecies of mammals have been identified in North America, but only three of these are different species of bears—the black bear, the polar bear, and the grizzly bear.

There are two types of grizzly bears. One is the grizzly that lives in the western United States, western and northwestern Canada, and throughout Alaska. This one is known as grizzly bear, silvertip, roachback; and just plain grizzly.

The other grizzly is the big brown bear that dwells on the Alaska Peninsula, the adjacent islands, and along a narrow strip of the Alaskan coast. It is also called Alaskan brown bear, brown grizzly, and Kodiak bear.

These two forms, or races, of grizzlies intergrade, and very often it is not possible to distinguish one from the other. The Alaskan brown bear is merely a coastal and island form of the grizzly and is consistently larger than the inland type.

In early days our western Indians called the grizzly the "white bear," and the Blackfeet referred to it as the "real bear" in order to distinguish it from the black bear. The smallest of the grizzlies evidently lived in the mountains of Mexico; those in the Far North attained the greatest size.

Meet the Grizzly Bear

The skull of the largest Alaskan brown bear officially measured was $17\frac{15}{16}$ inches long and $12\frac{13}{16}$ inches wide. Skulls found in contiguous United States are usually less than 15 inches long, although the skull of one California grizzly was $15\frac{6}{10}$ inches in length.

In describing the shape of a grizzly, certainly a picture is worth a thousand words. It has high, humped shoulders which result from the size and placement of the muscle mass above the shoulder blades. The black bear does not have this shoulder hump, and because of this the grizzly may be identified with certainty even at a distance by those who know the animal: the grizzly is highest at the shoulders, while the highest part of the black bear is the middle of its back.

The grizzly (left) has high humped shoulders. The black bear (below) does not; its highest part is the middle of the back.

A light-colored grizzly bear. Grizzlies may be very light in color, almost white.

Color is of little help in distinguishing between black and grizzly bears. However, if the fur is glossy black the bear is not a grizzly because the coat of a grizzly is never glossy. It may be very dark, almost black, and also it may be almost white. Actually the animal does not conform to any consistent coloration; therefore it cannot be identified by color alone.

Meet the Grizzly Bear

The very first grizzly I ever saw was very light tan, almost ivory white. In the same general area I observed a large bear that was nearly black and others that were brown. One evening a mother and two yearling cubs came to my bait, and I photographed all three of them. The female was very dark brown, one cub was lighter brown, and the other youngster was tan. Several grizzlies that I saw were uniformly dark with a light-brown throat patch.

I have seen a variety of color patterns on grizzlies. One adult had a white throat and a light-colored saddle-shaped area on its back; the rest of the bear was dark brown. Another grizzly had a very light stripe completely around its body, just behind its front legs. John M. Holzworth observed an Alaskan grizzly that was almost black but had a well-defined stripe along its left side from shoulder to rump, about halfway down. A number of grizzlies that I saw were dark or very dark on the shoulders, front and hind legs, and feet; the rest of the animals' bodies were light.

Some bears that I studied and photographed were dark with light-tipped guard hairs, and these appeared to be grizzled or silvery. This coloration may be responsible for the names of grizzly bear and silvertip.

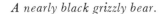

A nearly black grizzly bear.

A bald-faced grizzly.

One grizzly I photographed had an almost white face. The light area started at the front edge of the ears and extended forward. Bears with this coloration have been called bald-faced grizzlies. William H. Wright agreed with my findings, assuring us that grizzlies are all shades from almost jet black, through the browns and creams, to practically snow white. There are rarely two of the same color. He also noted that the hair on the entire head of some bears is light buff.

Other observers, too, have been impressed with the variety of colors of the grizzly. W. P. Hubbard saw a mother that was almost silvery white over her entire body, but both of her cubs were deep brown. In Wyoming, Mrs. Thelma Corder killed a male grizzly that had a white spot on its neck that ran back over the shoulder, and another white area that covered part of one side, rump, and leg. This bear was referred to as a "pinto."

The famous Alaskan guide, Allen E. Hasselborg, told of having seen several bears that were dark brown with a lemon yellow stripe running

Color may vary within the same family. This dark-colored mother had one dark- and one light-colored cub.

all the way down their sides from shoulder to rump, about four inches either side of the backbone.

In Montana I saw a very dark yearling with a prominent white collar completely around its neck. Holzworth, in Alaska, recorded a two-year-old with the same coloration. This seems to be a distinctive feature of many cubs, but the collar usually disappears with the first molt.

I have never seen or read of an albino grizzly bear. However, Joe Van Wormer, in his book, *The World of the Black Bear,* gave records of several albino black bears.

What color can we say is typical of the grizzly bear? It may be almost

This light-colored mother had three dark-colored cubs.

white or nearly black. It can be light brown, dark brown, tan, or cream-colored. It may be all one shade or it may have a color pattern of lights and darks. There is no typical color of the grizzly bear, but color variety in them is no more unusual than in other mammals, including man. The skin of the white man may be dark, medium, or light in color and may be pinkish, yellowish, or brownish; his hair may be black, red, blond, or brown, and it varies with age on the same individual.

Although the sizes, shapes, and colors of the grizzly may be observed from afar, details can be seen only at close quarters. For example, the tail is so short that it is scarcely visible in ordinary view, and I watched many grizzlies before I even noticed that they had tails. The claws on the front feet, though, are a different matter. The older and larger bears have the longest front claws, and some of these may be twice as long as the claws of yearling cubs. A huge grizzly, the largest one in my experience, also had the longest claws of any bear I ever saw. I very carefully estimated them to be six inches long. A grizzly killed by Lewis and Clark in Montana had claws 4⅜ inches long; those of another grizzly were 6¼ inches. These, of course, were the front claws, which are longer, and at times even twice as long as the hind ones.

Taxonomists at one time considered the claws as one of the means of identifying different kinds of big bears. But this is not a dependable character because claws, like color, vary greatly. Some grizzlies have very long claws that are strongly curved; others have claws that are rather short and blunt. The time of the year has a great deal to do with the length and even the curve of the bear's claws. In autumn, after a summer of digging for rodents on rocky hillsides, they are short and blunt. Even at this time, though, they are seldom less than two inches long, while those of the black bear are generally under two inches. In black bears, the hair extends almost to the tips of the claws, but at least three quarters of an inch of claw extends beyond the hairline on the foot of a grizzly. Usually the color of the big bear's talons is very light, yet I have seen some that were gray and others brown.

18

The tail of the grizzly is so short that it is hardly noticeable.

Cubs when about six months old have short, somewhat curved claws, and at this age they can climb trees. As they get older, the claws grow longer and straighter, and in their second summer, when they are year-lings, their front claws may be about two inches long. Both cubs and adults wear down their claws, and in late autumn they are short, blunt, and often broken. As you know, claws are merely fingernails and toenails, which continue to grow as do yours and mine. During the winter, when the bears are inactive, the claws keep on growing and are long and moderately pointed when the animals emerge from their dens in spring.

The front legs of the grizzly are quite long.

One thing I noticed about the grizzly bear is that its front legs appear to be quite long, possibly because the ankles are small and trim. Wright also noticed this and mentioned that the grizzly's forelegs differ from those of the black bear, being smaller in the ankle and marked by heavy, symmetrical development of muscle.

All bears are plantigrade, or flat-footed, as are humans, raccoons, woodchucks, and a number of other mammals. The grizzly has five well-developed toes on each of its four feet, and the claws are nonretractile. In this way the claws differ from those of a cat, which can extend or withdraw its claws at will.

The fingers of the raccoon are long and flexible, and it can use its paws like hands. This is not true of the grizzly, yet I have seen this bear pick up small objects and pieces of food with its front paws. In fact I was

Like woodchucks, raccoons, and man, the grizzly is plantigrade. This woodchuck is on the mound at the entrance of its burrow.

The grizzly can pick up small bits of food between its front toes and claws.

fortunate in getting photos of one grizzly holding a small portion of my bait between its front claws, and another sitting on its haunches holding a piece of meat between the palms of its hands. I have also seen captive bears drink soda from a bottle held between the front paws. However, the grizzly cannot clasp an object as we do with our hands because its paws are rather similar in construction to our feet.

21

The World of the Grizzly Bear

Because it is the largest flesh-eating mammal in the world, the grizzly bear has been and still is of great interest to sportsmen, naturalists, and others. The animal is indeed big, but its size and weight have been greatly overestimated. Lying prone, the adult grizzly is generally 6 to 8 feet and occasionally 9 feet long from the tip of its nose to the tail. Alaskan brown grizzlies have been killed that measured 9 feet 2 inches from nose to end of tail, and a Montana grizzly killed by Lewis and Clark was 9 feet from the nose to the tip of the absurdly short tail, which was probably only about 4 inches in length. Ernest Thompson Seton gave the following measurements for three grizzly bears killed in British Columbia: the length from the tip of the nose to the root of the tail of the first bear was 6 feet 3 inches; the second was 6 feet even; the third, 6 feet 7 inches.

A tall man is only 34 inches from the top of his head to his coccyx, or tailbone, so the length of the body of man is generally less than half and sometimes even less than a third of the length of the grizzly's body.

The front paws of the grizzly are more like the feet of humans: they cannot grasp an object the way humans can.

The grizzly is about 3 to 4½ feet high at the shoulders.

Standing on all four feet, the adult grizzly is about 3 to 4½ feet high at the shoulders. This means that the top of the shoulders of a large bear would touch the outstretched arms of a standing man. When in the same position as a grizzly bear, on all fours, a 6-foot man is only about 28 inches high at the shoulders.

The bear's chest is deeper and the circumference of its body is much greater than that of a man. Heavyweight boxing champion Cassius Clay has a 42½-inch chest measurement, while a medium-large grizzly measured 70½ inches around the chest. The neck measurement of this bear was 47 inches. Frank and John Craighead referred to a bear with a 40-inch neck. Man's neck is normally 15 to 16½ inches and rarely 18 inches in circumference.

The foot of a bear and that of a man are more nearly equal in length. The hind foot of the average grizzly is 10 to 13 inches long, and a very large bear may have a 16-inch foot. My foot is 10½ inches long and a friend who is 6 feet 2 inches tall has a foot that is 13¼ inches. However, the foot of a man is only about half as wide as that of the grizzly.

23

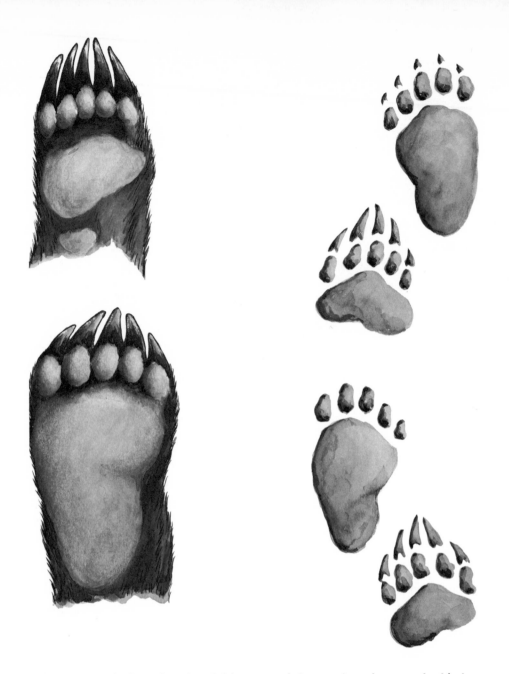

The claws on the front feet (top left) are much longer than those on the hind ones (bottom left). Claw marks (right) usually show in the tracks of the front feet. Imprints of the hind claws sometimes appear, although generally they do not.

Generally the size of the track of a bear is larger than the actual measurement of the foot because a foot spreads lengthwise and sidewise when supporting the weight of an animal. This fact is recognized by the

24

armed forces, and the soldier's shoes are fitted while he is standing and supporting a weight equal to his pack.

Some measurements made by me of the track of the hind foot of grizzlies, not including the claws, are 10½ by 7 inches and 12 by 7½ inches; the largest was 13 by 8 inches. Larry Koller gave the track measurement of an Alaskan bear as 16 inches long and 10 inches wide, and he wrote that the track was impressed about two inches deep in hard-packed sand. This is the largest track I know of.

Tracks of the hind foot seldom show any claw marks, but those of the front foot generally show five sizable claw prints. It is the front foot that bears the long, saberlike claws, and the track of this fore foot is much shorter than that of the hind foot.

Some animals, when walking, place their hind feet on the very same spots that had been occupied by the front feet. This produces a line of single tracks, of which the footprints in the snow of a red fox are an ideal example. The bear, however, does not walk in this fashion, and the prints of the front and back feet are usually separated so that the imprint of each of the four feet may be identified with certainty.

The length of the stride, or the distance between tracks, varies with the size of the bear; a large animal usually takes a longer step than a smaller one. I measured distances between tracks of both front and hind feet and found them to be about the same. My records show that some grizzlies when walking take a 21½-inch step; others, 22 to 26 inches; the longest stride was 27¾ inches.

Once a grizzly ran for a short distance in front of my car on a mountain road. One set of tracks of the running bear was 8 feet apart; the longest bound measured a little over 9 feet. Hasselborg wrote that the tracks of an Alaskan bear he wounded were 15 feet apart.

Often I have read that the face of the grizzly in profile is "dish-faced" and that the profile of the black bear is straight. Being an artist, I have done numerous portraits, and this statement interested me very much. I therefore made particular note of the faces of many black and grizzly

25

bears and found that they vary about as much as do those of humans. I saw bears with short snouts and long snouts; with straight muzzles and convex muzzles; some had slender snouts while others were heavy-jawed. In my opinion there is no typical profile for either species, and some black bears have profiles that are very similar to those of grizzlies and vice versa.

Bear profiles vary greatly. The profiles of some grizzlies are very similar to profiles of black bears and vice versa.

This grizzly has a long, slender snout.

The profile of this grizzly is quite straight.

This grizzly has a very straight profile.

Is this not true of man also? There is no typical human profile. Some people have long noses; others, short ones. Even identical twins differ, and it seems as though there are no two human faces exactly alike in the world.

The eyes of the grizzly bear are relatively small in comparison with those of some other mammals, for example, the deer and the antelope. Bears have eyelashes and the eyebrows of some may be quite pronounced;

27

Holzworth recorded an Alaskan grizzly with eyebrows 3 inches long. The pupil of the eye is round like a dog's and not vertical like a cat's.

The teeth of different mammals vary in size, shape, and number. The raccoon has a total of 40, the skunk 34, and the woodchuck only 22. Adult grizzlies normally have 42 teeth. In the upper jaw there are 6 incisors, 2 canines, 8 premolars, and 4 molars. In the lower jaw the number of teeth are the same except for the molars, which number 6.

The eyes of the grizzly are small and the pupils are round.

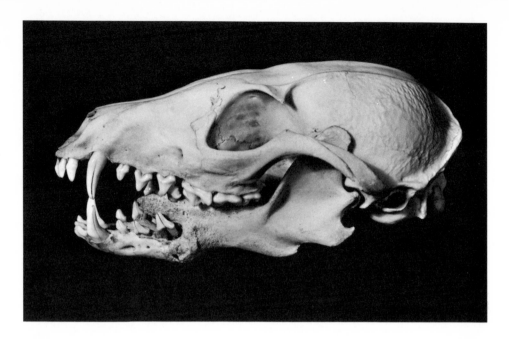

Bear's skull, showing the teeth. The lower jaw was completely broken on both sides, perhaps by a bullet, a fight, or an accident. Whatever the cause, the bone knit and the injury healed.

It is often possible to determine the kind of food that an animal eats by the size and shape of its teeth. Rodents such as woodchucks and beavers are plant-eaters and have broad, chisel-like front teeth suitable for gnawing. Bears, besides plants, eat flesh, and like dogs and cats they have strong, sharp, pointed teeth adapted for biting, tearing, and masticating. Although the total number of teeth is normally forty-two, they are of different kinds and serve different purposes. The incisors, which are those in the front and center of the mouth, are used for biting or shearing just as those same front teeth of humans can be used for biting off a smaller piece of bread from a full slice. The canine teeth are the fangs, or tusks, and they are the equal of the human eyeteeth. Bears employ their fangs for tearing, gripping, and holding, for example, in catching and holding a salmon. These grizzly fangs may be as long as 2½ inches. The molars are the chewing or grinding teeth, and they function just about the same as yours and mine.

Being a mammal, the grizzly has mammary glands, or teats, that are capable of milk production so that a mother can nourish her young. On each side of the chest of the female there are two nipples, often called pectoral mammae. These are quite wide apart. On each side of the belly there is one nipple; there are called inguinal mammae. The four pectoral mammae plus the two inguinal mammae make a total of six teats, and there are sufficient to suckle the offspring, which most often number two.

The coat of the grizzly bear, like that of many other mammals, is composed of rather thick, fleecy underfur with long, coarse, projecting guard hairs. These hairs in the shaggy winter coat are 3 inches long or more, and they are shed annually along with the underfur. Hair in the grizzly bear's sleeping chamber reveals that shedding begins even before bears leave their winter dens, but cubs do not shed during their first year. When grizzlies leave their lairs in the spring, they rub off their fur. Hunters complain about this because up to 50 per cent of the spring hides are disfigured and, of course, make less attractive trophy rugs. Many sportsmen, therefore, prefer to hunt in the fall, for at this time the grizzly's old, faded coat has been replaced with one that is new, long-haired, and in excellent condition.

Man, who stands upright, has more hair on his chest than on his back. Bears, and most other four-footed mammals that walk in a horizontal position, have the most dense fur on their backs; often their bellies are scantily haired. This seems to be for protection, because the upper side or the back may be pelted with rain and hail and also covered with snow; the hair of the back is also protection from damaging rays of the sun.

As insulation, hair keeps heat in, and it also keeps heat out. An insulated house is cooler in summer and warmer in winter. Likewise, a mammal is cooler in summer and warmer in winter because of its fur. During cold weather, the thick fur on the back of a grizzly resting or sleeping in a procumbent position is like a wool blanket covering the beast. When I was young I never wore a hat, and my hair kept my head warm in winter and cool in summer. Now that my hair is rather scant I need a hat for warmth in winter, and if my head is exposed to hot summer sun-

The coat of the grizzly is composed of thick, fleecy underfur with projecting long guard hairs. This animal is wearing its new fall and winter coat.

A big grizzly standing on its hind legs may be 9 feet tall.

shine, I feel the heat and a small spot on my scalp actually gets sun-burned.

All who know the grizzly agree that it varies widely in color from almost white to nearly black, and there is even greater variation in its weight. There are small bears and big bears and bigger bears. A large female may be smaller than a small male, because males are larger than females, and a young adult is generally not as heavy as an older individual of the same sex.

A big grizzly standing on its hind legs may be 9 feet tall; no man, so far as I know, has ever attained this height. Even though it is huge, the grizzly bear appears to be larger than it really is. Ernest Thompson Seton, while watching a good-sized grizzly, guessed that its height at the shoulders was at least 4 feet; however, the bear, without stooping, walked under a horizontal branch which Seton found to be only 35 inches from the ground. Estimates of weight have been just as erroneous, and though I have heard of 2,000-pound grizzlies there are no authentic records of any.

In my home town of Kingston, New York, Schoentag's saloon was a place where many of the local sportsmen gathered. Each autumn deer and bear that had been taken in the nearby Catskill Mountains were displayed in front of the saloon. Shortly before the First World War a huge bear was hung on the game rack, and a contest to guess the bear's weight was started. Each of the hunters put a dollar in the pool, and the one making the nearest estimate of the weight of the animal won the pool. Most of the men guessed that the bear weighed from 500 to 600 pounds, and a few of the estimates were higher.

At the close of the contest a steelyard was used for the weighing, and it was found that the bear weighed 387 pounds. The animal had been drawn, or "hog dressed." Since that time I have weighed black bears before and after they have been eviscerated, and I have found that the live weight of a bear can be closely determined by adding 25 per cent of the drawn weight to the weight of the eviscerated carcass. Therefore, the live weight of that big black bear would have been approximately 483 pounds. All of the contestants, as is usual, had overestimated the weight of the bear.

Seton told of a similar incident. An enormous grizzly in Union Park, Chicago, was so well fed by park visitors that in his later years he could only crawl about. Estimates of the animal's weight ran from 2,000 to

2,200 pounds. However, the bear's actual weight was found to be 1,153 pounds, only about half of some of the guessed weights.

There are many accurate measurements of big game animals taken in the field, because a tape measure is small and light in weight. However, there are very few authentic weight records of large wild animals, because weighing equipment and hoisting tackle are heavy and cumbersome. Most given weights have been estimates made by hunters and guides, and though these are of no scientific value they are the ones that seem to have established the records. The integrity of these men is not questioned here, but their ability to guess the weight of an animal certainly is. Many thousands of people have been weighed, and the weight of man is well known. Even so, can you accurately judge the weight of any person? In my opinion, accurate weights of individual grizzlies are more satisfactory than general conclusions and estimated averages.

Robert L. Rausch, in his work on Arctic mammals, stated that the largest bears live on Kodiak and Afognak islands and the Alaska Peninsula. The greatest reliable weight of which he knew was 1,200 pounds. He wrote that weights of 1,500 pounds are frequently reported, but these are estimates. The largest grizzly of which zoo director William T. Hornaday had an authentic record was the Chicago zoo specimen that weighed 1,153 pounds. Another zoo animal, Monarch, weighed 1,127 pounds after death. Seton gave a weight of 916 pounds for a grizzly taken in Yellowstone National Park in May with one arrow by Arthur Young. Concerning this bear, Dr. Saxton Pope wrote:

As we dismembered him, we weighed the parts. The veins were absolutely dry of blood, and without this substance, which represents a loss of nearly 10 per cent of his weight, he was 916 pounds. There was hardly an inch of fat on his back. At the end of autumn, this adipose layer would be nearly 6 inches thick. He would then have weighed over 1,400 pounds.

Here are weights of some grizzlies in the National Zoological Park,

Washington, D.C.: one adult male weighed 730 pounds, another male weighed 514 pounds at the age of three and one-half years, and an adult female weighed 325 pounds. Colonel W. D. Pickett claimed that he actually weighed forty grizzlies and the heaviest was less than 800 pounds. One from Yellowstone Park, kept in the Washington Zoo, weighed 730 pounds in September: captive bears also gorge in the fall.

Robert MacGowan, a Canadian hunter, told me that he killed two grizzlies in British Columbia. One weighed 368 and the other 422 pounds. His partner, John Reilly, shot one that weighed 763 pounds. This was the biggest grizzly of which MacGowan knew, and it measured 7 feet 2 inches from nose to tail. Frank and John Craighead, in the summer of 1959, recorded a tranquilized Yellowstone grizzly that weighed 520 pounds.

It is true that the grizzly bear is big, but when its skin is stretched out, as for a rug, it is enormous. Harold McCracken killed an Alaskan grizzly whose hide measured 11 feet 4 inches long and 10 feet 4 inches wide from claw to claw of the front feet. Old Four Toes, the Colorado outlaw, was 12 feet long. Writing about four Alaskan grizzlies, Seton stated that the length of the skin of one was 13 feet 6 inches, another measured 11 feet, the third bear was 10 feet 6 inches, and the last one was 9 feet 4 inches.

It is generally agreed that today the largest bears are the big brown grizzlies in southwestern Alaska, on Kodiak Island, and the Alaska Peninsula. There are reasons why the same species may be larger or smaller in different parts of its range. Food is often a more important factor than climate, and sometimes the quality of the food is more important than the quantity. Where food is plentiful and of proper character, the animals are big and healthy, without regard to the climate.

Where the big brown grizzly thrives, there is a persistent abundance of salmon and a luxurious growth of coastal vegetation, so this animal has both quantity and quality of food. The salmon produces an unlimited supply of high-protein nourishment, and this is size-building. In captivity, black bears quickly attain enormous proportions when fed a high-protein diet, just as the brown bear in Alaska has done.

Variations in the size of an animal in different parts of its range are not unusual. In some streams in New York State, the brook trout, *Salvelinus fontinalis,* has not been known to exceed 7 inches in length, yet in Canadian waters I have caught brook trout that measured up to 19 inches. The largemouthed black bass, *Micropterus salmoides,* is another example. In New York State this fish seldom, if ever, attains the weight of 8 pounds, but in Florida it may be as heavy as 25 pounds.

Age also affects the size and weight of the grizzly bear. Although it may reach sexual maturity when about three and a half years of age, it does not attain full growth until eight or ten years old. An Alaskan cub of the coastal and island form in the National Zoo at Washington, D.C., was 180 pounds when one year old, 450 pounds at two years, 625 in his third year, 770 at four years, 970 when five, 1,050 in his sixth year, and 1,200 pounds when nine years old.

The life span of the grizzly, like that of all other creatures, varies with individuals. It has been estimated that about five times the number of years required to reach sexual maturity is the approximate potential length of life of the species. The grizzly bear breeds first at three to five years of age, so that its normal life span may be about 15 to 25 years. In the Bronx Zoo, Ivan the Terrible, an Alaskan grizzly, died of old age. He had lived in the zoo for nearly 30 years. Monarch was not born there but lived in the San Francisco Zoo for 22 years. Other captive grizzlies were known to have attained the ages of 26, 27½, and 30 years. In the National Zoological Park, Washington, D.C., big bears survived for 16, 18, 19, and 24 years. In the Bronx Zoo, New York, a grizzly born in 1903 died in 1924, at the age of 21½ years. Another died in 1946, when it was 24½ years old. Frank and John Craighead claimed that in Yellowstone National Park a few bears live to 25 or 30, but the average life span may be only 5 or 6 years.

It seems that grizzlies in the wild seldom, if ever, attain ages as great as those in captivity. But what causes the death of a wild, free grizzly? Russel Annabel, the Alaskan guide, found the remains of two old grizzlies that had died in their dens. Enos A. Mills discovered a grizzly that had perished in a forest fire, another in a desert flood, one which was killed at the foot of a cliff by a falling rock, and another that had been crushed in a snow slide. The Craigheads claimed that bears die of starvation, from the elements, diseases, old age, mortal combat, and, of course, from the bullets of hunters.

In Yellowstone National Park there is a small, gloomy ravine in which many creatures have perished because of poisonous gas emitted from rocky vents. Remains of grizzlies, elk, and many smaller mammals have been found there. Professor T. A. Jaggar, Jr., described the area as "Death Gulch, A Natural Bear Trap," and wrote that it was a

. . . frightfully weird and dismal place, utterly without life, and occupied by only a tiny streamlet and an appalling odour. We at length discovered some brown furry masses lying scattered about the floor of the ravine. Approaching cautiously, it became quickly evident that we had before us a large group of huge recumbent Bears; the one nearest us was lying with his nose between his paws, facing us, and so exactly like a huge Dog asleep that it did not seem possible that it was the sleep of death. To make sure, I threw a pebble at the animal, striking him on the flank; the distended skin sounded like a drum-head, and the only response was a belch of poisonous gas that almost overwhelmed us. Closer examination showed that the animal was a young Silver-tip Grizzly (*Ursus horribilis*); a few drops of thick, dark-red blood stained his nostrils and the ground beneath. There proved to be 5 other carcasses, all Bears in various stages of decay; careful search revealed oval areas of hair and bones that represented 2 other Bears, making a total of 8 carcasses in all. Seven were Grizzlies, one was a Cinnamon Bear [a color form of the black bear]. . . . One huge Grizzly was so recent a victim that his tracks were still visible in the white, earthy slopes leading down to the spot where he had met his death. In no case were any marks of violence seen, and there can be no question that death was occasioned by the gas.

The World of the Grizzly Bear

The grizzly bear, like man and other mammals, has the five known senses of sight, smell, hearing, taste, and touch. Some naturalists add a sixth sense which is an extraordinary sense of perception. Certain senses are more highly developed in some species of animals than in others, depending upon the need, and subsequent adaptation for survival. For example, a forest-dwelling animal like the deer has a keen sense of hearing and smell which enables it to detect the approach of an enemy through dense cover long before it comes into view. Visibility in a forest is limited, so the forest animal's sight may not be as well developed as that of a plains dweller like the pronghorn. This animal's eyesight is so sharp that it can recognize friend or foe at a great distance across the open plains and prairies.

Deer are forest dwellers, and their senses of hearing and smell are well developed. Their ears are large and cup-shaped and can be turned to detect sounds.

The pronghorn is a plains dweller and has a highly developed sense of sight.

Because of its size and strength the grizzly had nothing to fear in its natural habitat until the sixteenth century, when the white man invaded its North American world. The grizzly had never been dependent upon its senses for survival, and well-developed senses of sight, smell, and hearing had not been needed. Its attitude toward other animals was one of indifference, and it wandered around unmolested. Other animals sneaked off or fled when the grizzly approached because it is the King of the American Wilderness. Bear against man in a state of nature would have been no contest, but man with his high-powered weapons of destruction is supreme. Apparently grizzlies have learned this and they avoid man whenever possible. On most of its range, the grizzly has become more dependent on its sight, smell, and hearing in its defense, because it is a hunted animal, unable to cope with the long-range modern gun.

39

Compared with the pronghorn, the eyesight of the grizzly is very poor. As I crouched in plain view in the open, bears have passed quite close without recognizing me. Once when I was attempting to photograph pronghorns, a grizzly came out of a gully not more than two hundred yards away. I was sitting on the ground and did not move. The animal passed at about a hundred feet, and though there was no tall grass, trees, or bushes between us, it apparently did not see me. Another time I stood motionless, close to a large tree, and a grizzly walked by at about twenty yards without detecting my presence. However, the bear got my scent after it had passed; when perhaps sixty yards away, it rose on its hind feet and looked about. Still it did not see me, but my scent was enough to warn it, and the animal galloped away.

It is evident that the grizzly does not have the acute sense of hearing of the deer. Its ears are relatively small and not very flexible; the deer has large cupped ears that can be turned about so that sound may be detected regardless of the direction from which it comes.

Although its eyesight and hearing may be secondary, the grizzly has a keen sense of smell, which was the direct cause for some of my failures to photograph the animal. One night I waited in concealment near my bait, a forequarter of mutton. Because I did not move there was no sound to betray my presence. Although I could not see details of my surroundings in the dark, I could make out the forms of tree trunks, logs, and large rocks. Suddenly I recognized the bulk of a huge bear circling by bait slowly and silently. When it got my scent, it flattened itself on its belly. There it remained, not more than a hundred feet away, for at least fifteen minutes. The scent of the mutton was attractive to the hungry bear, but the dangerous human smell was stronger. The grizzly did not come to my bait that night, and I got no picture.

Once, while hiding at the edge of a forest, I watched a grizzly bear searching for food on an open slope about two hundred feet away. Deliberately I broke a small dry stick, to see if the sound would alert the bear, but it did not react. Then I threw a small branch into the

After grizzlies had become accustomed to me and my scent in connection with the food I placed for them, they tolerated my presence and often I was able to photograph at quite close quarters.

underbrush. Still the bear did not respond. One day, under similar conditions and at about the same distance I tested a white-tailed deer. When I snapped a small twig, it quickly bounded away. It is possible that the bear I was watching did not respond because it was intent in its search for food, or the sounds may not have carried to the animal. Also, it is well known that acuteness of the senses may vary with individual animals. One bear may be able to see, smell, and hear better than another.

It occurred to me that I might have more success if I used a method that has aided me in obtaining photographs of smaller animals. On the ground, near the grizzly bait, I dropped an outdoor shirt I had been wearing that was saturated with my odor. For a few nights the meat was not taken by the bears, but on the sixth night it was gone. After that the grizzlies came to the bait that I put out, regardless of the shirt and my odor, and when I concealed myself nearby they disregarded me. It seemed that they had learned to associate my scent with the food, and to disregard the "man-odor."

41

The World of the Grizzly Bear

Holzworth found that when in sight of man a bear will often work around to the windward in order to get the scent which will tell him of his danger more clearly than his eyesight can. Hasselborg believed that a bear will get the scent of a man at twelve feet, no matter how the wind is blowing. He said that a grizzly had picked up his scent trail fourteen hours after he had passed. Hunters know only too well that it is practically impossible to get near a bear if the breeze is blowing from the hunter toward the animal.

Birds sing, coyotes bark, and squirrels chatter, but the grizzly bear is one of the most silent animals I know. However, I have heard them grunt and utter low growls when another bear came too close. One night a medium-sized grizzly not more than eight feet from me uttered a rather quiet "woof." Others who have heard the bear describe its vocal sounds variously as a cough, growl, moan, whine, sniff, groan, roar, bellow, bawl, snarl, and huffing sound. Usually, however, bears are relatively silent, except when seriously disturbed or wounded when the sounds they utter are low, mainly conversational.

By comparison with man, the strength of some animals is phenomenal, and the grizzly bear is possibly the strongest land mammal in North America. This is due to its enormous size and weight, plus the fact that the animal is exercising by walking or running wherever it goes, while man usually rides. Also the grizzly must dig, when digging is necessary, for food or for the shelter of a winter den. All of these strenuous activities develop its power and keep it physically fit.

Enos A. Mills told of a grizzly brought to bay by dogs and horsemen. The bear charged and broke the jaw of one horse with one stroke of its forepaw and with a second blow caved in three ribs of another. Mills also reported that he had known bears to drag the carcass of a cow or steer twice their own weight. He also included an account of a grizzly that was roped by cowboys in Montana. The bear pulled one horse off its feet and dragged it along the ground, and the strain on the second rope, tied to the saddle horn, caused the cinches to break. To this Seton

42

added a similar account. In California some cowboys surprised a grizzly in the open, and two of them succeeded in putting the loops of their lariats around the bear's neck. The horses braced, but the grizzly brought all its mighty strength into play and, in spite of the choking, dragged the two horses after it. The cowboys were forced to cut the bear loose. Seton also wrote that in the bull rings in early California one bear was known to have killed six bulls in an afternoon. The maddened bear, standing on its hind legs, struck each of the bulls dead with a single blow between the eyes.

The grizzly is regarded as the strongest land mammal in North America.

A bull elk, which weighs as much as 750 pounds, can be carried bodily by the mighty grizzly.

Moose may weigh 1,400 pounds and even 1,800 pounds in Alaska. The giant grizzly can carry and drag the carcass of one of these big animals.

Victor H. Cahalane asserted that a large grizzly quite often picks up its prey, even an elk or moose, and carries it bodily to a place it has chosen in which to feed on the dead animal. An adult elk may weigh 750 pounds; a cow moose, 800 pounds; a bull moose, 1,400 pounds, or even 1,800 pounds in Alaska.

Regardless of its bulk and great strength, the grizzly or any other large formidable wild animal can be quickly destroyed with modern high-powered weapons. In the early days the smooth-bore gun was a poor weapon against the grizzly, and because of this it was generally accepted that the bear was able to withstand terrible punishment. W. P. Hubbard, a big-game hunter himself, has assured us that the grizzly bear cannot survive the bullets of a high-powered rifle any more than deer or elk, and is just as easily killed as any other game. William H. Wright, who killed more than a hundred grizzlies, agreed, contending that the bear cannot begin to stand up under the rain of bullets that an old Rocky Mountain goat can survive. Mills added that the grizzly is not an exceedingly difficult animal to kill if shot in a vital spot—in the upper part of the heart, in the brain, or through the center of the shoulder spine.

There is no animal on land or in the ocean that cannot be killed with man's terribly destructive inventions. The enormous whale succumbs to the harpoon carrying an explosive charge. The elephant and the rhinoceros are downed by one well-placed bullet. The fact that a grizzly can be killed by man does not detract from its nobleness and terrifying strength. All animals, including man himself, are vulnerable.

Generally it appears that smaller animals run faster than larger ones, and the speed of the big grizzly is often underestimated. Once when driving on a forest road I came suddenly upon a grizzly. It took off in high gear, and I sounded my horn to keep it running. By glancing at the speedometer and at the bear, I was able to determine that the animal was running between 33 and 34 miles per hour. The race was a short one because the bear ran off the road and into the forest. I paced the distance and estimated that the animal had galloped about 97 yards in front of my car.

Seton stated that, for fifty or a hundred yards, a grizzly can go as fast as a good horse, and in rough country it can run faster than any horse, and keep it up indefinitely. When covering a full mile on a track, a race horse runs at about 34 miles an hour. Horses not bred for racing, when running over uneven terrain, do not come near this speed. It is probable, therefore, that a grizzly can run as fast as or even faster than a horse in rough country. It can definitely travel faster than a man who runs a hundred yards in ten seconds on a smooth track, for at this rate the speed of the runner is only 29.3 miles per hour.

The gait of a grizzly running at top speed is a gallop. Its slow gait is a walk, and its intermediate gait is a lope. The grizzly, like some horses, is therefore a three-gaited animal. I have seen the grizzly in full gallop only a few times. Like most mammals it usually walks, sometimes

This grizzly is walking rapidly. Bears are three-gaited and walk, lope, and gallop.

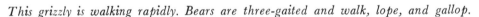

plodding rather slowly and at other times stepping along briskly. The lope, which is faster than the walk and slower than the gallop, is an easy, ground-covering, bounding gait that seems not to tire the bear. Many times I have watched grizzlies loping along across flats, up slopes, and down slopes, always maintaining a steady pace.

In late evening, before dark, a mother and two yearlings came each day to my bait from a forest more than a mile away. When they emerged from the woods they were always loping and never slackened their pace until within about fifty yards of the meat. Then the mother would rise up on her hind legs, look about, and sniff the breeze. From there the family walked to my bait.

In a standing position the female looked tall and she was; add the length of her hind legs to her 6- or 7-foot body and she was 8 or 9 feet in height. Tracy I. Storer asserted that, when standing, a large grizzly can reach to a height of 9 or 10 feet. Seton wrote that a grizzly bear in the National Zoo at Washington could take an apple in its mouth from the end of a stick held at the height of 9 feet 3 inches.

I have seen many grizzly bears standing on their hind legs, but I have never seen one walk while in this position. However, there is no doubt that they can walk on their hind legs because bears have been trained to dance in an upright position and also to roller-skate. Holzworth, who had been close to a great many Alaskan grizzlies, believed as I do that they can walk on their hind feet and possibly do in some instances.

Hasselborg once shot an Alaskan grizzly. With a deep roar the beast leaped up and then rose on its hind legs hardly ten feet from the hunter. Another bullet, quickly fired, smashed into the bear's ribs and heart. The great beast took several steps forward, walking on its hind feet and pawing the air. Then it sank to the ground.

One of the useful purposes of the grizzly's powerful forelegs and long claws is for digging. It digs deeper and faster than the black bear, and it turns over great quantities of soil in its hunt for burrowing animals. Slopes in Alaska are pitted with holes, each big enough to bury a piano,

47

Grizzy bears stand on their hind feet, but I have never seen one walk while in this position.

from which hibernating ground squirrels have been routed and devoured by grizzlies.

When I first saw holes that had been excavated by this fur-clad giant, I did not know what they were. I had seen big bears turn over rocks and small boulders in their search for food, but it was not until one September day that I saw for the first time a grizzly dig out a ground squirrel. It seemed to me that the bear worked terribly hard for a meal that consisted of an animal which weighed only about one pound.

The black bear has one talent that the grizzly bear does not—an ability to climb. Lou Ovitt, a French-Canadian guide, once said to me jokingly: "A sure way to tell what kind of a bear it is, is to climb a tree. If the bear climbs up after you and claws your hide a bit, it ain't no grizzly." And Ovitt was right. Adult grizzly bears do not climb trees.

William H. Wright verified this and stated that grown grizzlies do not climb trees. They do walk out on a leaning tree and they are expert walkers on fallen logs and timber, so they have a good sense of balance. Seton added that the mature grizzly never climbs and that he never leaps from a rock; he always finds a way to get down afoot.

I have never seen an adult or a yearling grizzly climb a tree, although I have seen dozens of black bears, young and old, climb up and down both large and small trees. In fact black bears are expert tree-climbers and they seem almost to run up a tree when in great haste.

On two different occasions I saw grizzly cubs climb. They were not more than six or seven months old, and they went up the trees just for the fun of it. One youngster climbed an aspen to a height of about 8 feet, where it clung for a few seconds and then descended, tail first. On the second occasion, two cubs climbed a slightly slanted tree. One youngster reached a height of perhaps 6 feet, and the other one was just below it. Each of these grizzly cubs seemed to climb just as well as young black bears and, like them, they backed down. I have never seen any bear descend head first, but I have observed woodchucks, squirrels, and even raccoons descend from trees head first.

Contrary to the opinions and observations of all hunters, naturalists, and scientists is the statement of Raymond J. Kramer. He wrote that on Kodiak Island, Alaska, he found an adult big brown bear 10 feet up on the first limb of a large cottonwood tree. Twenty feet above her was a cub of about eighty pounds. When he attempted to photograph the bear it came down the tree trunk, head first, in a threatening rush.

I know of no mammal which cannot swim, but some are more expert than others. Once I saw a little brown bat shot by a scientific collector while it was flying over Lake Placid, New York. The wounded animal fell into the water and at once began to swim toward the shore. I have also seen many other animals swim, including mice, woodchucks, otter, deer, moose, and even porcupines. The black bear readily takes to water, and I have seen a mother and her two cubs plunge into a swift-flowing river and swim about sixty feet to the opposite shore. However, I have seen only one grizzly swim, and this animal merely wanted to get to the land on the other side of the stream. Others have also seen the big bear swim; Enos A. Mills reported that in Alaska he saw a grizzly in the ocean swimming vigorously between two islands that were seven miles apart. John Bidwell related that a female grizzly swam out to sea after her mate had been shot and killed, then turned and headed back toward the shore. The grizzly bear can swim, and the way in which it gambols about in salmon streams proves that it has no fear of water. Often, when attempting to catch a fish in its mouth, the bear ducks its head under water, and at times its body is completely submerged.

Mills described an instance in which a grizzly was swimming and playing at the same time. The bear was juggling an eight-foot log in a mountain stream. Once it hugged the log between its fore paws, stood it on end in the water, and tried to climb it. Then it lay across the log and splashed about like a boy on a pole trying to learn to swim. Mills wrote that, generally, the grizzly plays alone. Three or four times he saw one playing much after the manner of a dog. It ran around and around in a small circle, leaping in the air and dodging about. Then it rolled on its back with its four feet waving in the air. Two grizzly cubs that Mills raised were always eager for play. They played with each other and also with Mills, and one of them occasionally played with the dog.

I once saw a medium-sized grizzly lying on its back in a rather open pine forest. The bear's feet were up in the air and it was playing with its toes much like a baby in a crib doing the same thing.

Mills mentioned that a grizzly goes out of its way in order to coast down steep, snowy places. Hubbard also commented on this and wrote:

I have seen many bear toboggan slides, but Ed Francis, aged trapper and prospector of Alaska's Tanana River country, was the first to tell me of seeing a bear in the act of tobogganing.

An open slope, snow-covered to a depth of about two feet, angled downward for almost a hundred feet. At the foot of the slope was a snow-packed gully. The bear stepped off the trail, sat down at the top of the slope, raised his hind paws a little, leaned somewhat forward, wiggled his body, and suddenly went shooting down amid a flurry of fine snow. He hit the snow bank at the bottom and went end over middle.

Like a child with a new sled, he turned about and started up the slope. At the top he sat down on his haunches and looked down at his tracks in the snow. He moved to the crest of the slope, as he had done before, sat down, gave a wiggle with his body to get started, and down he went aflying. Then he moved off down the gully.

One day in summer I saw two grizzly cubs, perhaps seven months old, wrestling and playing like kittens or puppies. However, I have never seen yearlings or adults playing except once. This was near the end of August, and a mother and two cubs about one and a half years old were coming regularly to my bait. Late one afternoon I saw the family searching for food in the flatlands. Soon the mother bear and her off-spring were joined by a dark-colored male that might have been the father of the cubs. He pushed one of the youngsters and rolled it over. At once the two smaller bears rushed him, and the adult male and the cubs rolled about in a good-natured wrestling bout. The mother sat down, took her toes in her front paws, and rocked back and forth as she watched. Through my binocular I could see what was surely a smile on her face.

The three wrestlers moved toward the female, and the male, holding off the cubs at arm's length, suddenly gave the mother a push and she rolled over three times. Then the group galloped off a short distance and began to search for food. I took a photograph of the family, and though it was a long shot it showed the mother, the young, and the dark-colored male.

For centuries the African lion has been known as the King of Beasts, and more recently the grizzly bear has been designated the King of Beasts in North America. Those who know and respect him have said that he is noble, dignified, magnificent in his strength, courageous, independent, intelligent, curious, wise, and fearless. Some believe that grizzlies are more curious than any of the other animals, and it does seem that the grizzly's interest in its surroundings is greater than that of the average human. It is generally agreed that most grizzlies have greater knowledge of the habits of humans than people have of the habits of bears. If this were not true, perhaps the big bear would more easily be killed by hunters. The curiosity of the huge beast is not idle, indeed not. For its own survival the bear must be concerned about anything that may benefit or harm it.

In its study of people, one bear stopped and watched Mrs. J. J. Stevensen for about an hour while she was sitting and sewing outside her cabin. And once when I was making an oil painting of some western scenery I became aware of a grizzly bear that was watching me. The animal sat on the ground in back of me and gazed with evident interest while I worked. Once it stood up on its hind legs for a better view and then sat down again. I was aware of the bear's presence for fully fifteen minutes, and I do not know how long it was there before I noticed it. The animal was at the edge of a forest about fifty yards from me, and I was in the open. When I left the scene, I walked slowly away while the grizzly sat and watched me go.

While photographing bears in Alaska, Holzworth waded slowly up a salmon stream. Hasselborg, the guide, motioned for him to turn around and as he did so a big bear crashed into the brush. Hasselborg said the huge animal had been standing on its haunches behind a stump not fifteen feet away, watching the activities of the photographer with interest.

Meet the Grizzly Bear

Curiosity is associated with the desire and the ability to learn, and this is a sign of intelligence. "From sunrise to sunset," wrote Dr. William T. Hornaday, one-time director of the Bronx Zoo in New York, "a bear is an animal of original thought and vigorous enterprise. Put a normal bear in any new situation that you please, he will try to make himself master of it." Hornaday then listed twenty of the most intelligent animals and rated them according to their intelligence based upon ten factors. The chimpanzee rated highest with a score of 926 out of a possible 1,000. The grizzly bear was given a rating of 725 out of the 1,000, rating higher than the gorilla, rhinoceros, white-tailed deer, bighorn sheep, tiger, wolf, coyote, red fox, and even the wolverine. The grizzly had a low rating in memory, with only 25 out of a possible 100, while the chimpanzee was perfect with a score of 100. But the grizzly got 100 for its powers of reasoning, whereas the chimp got only 75.

Mother and two yearling cubs.

The white-tailed deer is wise and cautious, but the grizzly has a greater intelligence rating.

Renowned for its wisdom, the red fox has a lower intelligence rating than the grizzly.

Enos A. Mills's two pet grizzly cubs had the capacity and the desire to learn. About them he wrote:

One June morning, I came upon two tiny grizzly cubs, each about the size of a cottontail rabbit. I took them to my cabin. In 24 hours Jenny knew that her name was Jenny and Johnny that his name was Johnny.

Young bear cubs are the most wide-awake and observing little people that I know of. Never have I seen a horse or dog who understood as readily or learned as rapidly as these two bears.

It appears that most human beings believe they are mentally superior to all other animals and that only man is capable of having feelings, emotions, and sentiments. Adherents of this school generally believe that all creatures except man are guided solely by instinct and not by intellect. Therefore, a mother grizzly cannot experience maternal love for her cubs or a dog devotion for its master.

Our knowledge and understanding is continually increasing, and more and more scientists agree that there is more similarity between man and other mammals than anatomy. Proof is available that some animals other than man have the power to reason. They possess intellect, and those who understand animals realize that mammals can communicate with others of their own kind. Some of them are courageous, affectionate, and even humorous. As with man, however, individuals in any species vary. Ernest Thompson Seton wrote: "Wise Grizzlies and super-wise there always were, and mediocre and fools. But the fools went early; they were weeded out by the hunters as soon as repeating rifles appeared. The stupid and the commonplace went next, and the ten-times-sifted remnant are the wisest of the wise in their kind."

We have learned that the lives of animals are not controlled by instinct alone. Perhaps instinct is most obvious in the behavior of most birds. For example, swallows instinctively make a nest that has been the same for centuries, and a chicken, without learning, can do nearly everything at birth that it will ever be able to do. But mammals are capable of learning new ways and of showing more individual behavior. Like birds, men and bears are helpless at birth. They are also dependent on their parents during the early part of their lives, but if they are to survive they must go beyond instincts and learn their lessons of life as they grow. Neither man nor bear is born with ready-made intelligence, only the potential to develop it. Today man has the same brain as the cave man had. There has been no change in its structure, but it has greatly improved with use. The brain of the grizzly bear has also improved with use, and this hastened because of the Spanish settlements in the West in the early 1800's. Before that time the Indian with his short-range bow was not a threat, and up to the days of the repeating rifle the grizzly wandered boldly and indifferently over his domain, day and night. There was nothing for him to fear.

He was quick to learn, though, that man with his newly acquired and powerful gun was a dangerous threat, and he adjusted accordingly. He also encountered the steel trap and quickly learned to avoid it. Seton wrote: "The Grizzly that is not trap-wise as well as man-wise is rare today and passing." He then quoted William Wells of Wyoming:

In the old days the Bear was a beast of the open country, a daylight traveller, seeking his food when and how he pleased. Up until along in the early '80's, Bears were not hunted much; but along about '89, the skins took a jump in price, and at the same time some of the Western states put a bounty on Bruin. This made hunting them profitable, and they commenced to decrease rapidly. From this time on Bears began to change their habits greatly. A Bear nowadays keeps pretty well under cover. During the day he finds the thickest brush or timber that he can, and there he stays, slipping away quietly at the slightest suspicious noise. It used to be that if a Bear heard or saw something that he did not understand, he would stand up on his hind legs to look. And if suddenly startled he would often, after running a way, stop and stand up to look back. But now a Bear that hears a human voice hardly ever stops to look, but gets away on the jump.

When following one of its trails, the grizzly's intelligence often becomes apparent. Every little while, the bear may make a circuit to the side and rear, in order to get to the windward of its own back trail and in this way assure itself that no danger follows.

According to Seton the grizzly can be and has been completely domesticated, but the black bear never wholly and successfully. The black bear usually grows cranky and unreliable as it reaches maturity, while the grizzly has not been guilty of treachery. Its tameness, when it is tame, is of that gentle, flawless kind that we look for in the dog. A grizzly captured when full-grown, though, cannot be tamed.

In my youth I saw a number of bears being led about on city streets by the owners, who often played an accordion. These were known as dancing bears, and they often appeared on the vaudeville stage. It was said that these were grizzly bears and also Russian bears, which are one of the grizzlies. I have never seen a performing black bear. Today, the trained bears that roller-skate and ride bicycles belong to the grizzly bear family.

As early as 1847, in San Jose, a partly tamed grizzly was tied to a tree. In San Francisco, in 1853, a captive grizzly took small pieces of meat from his keeper's fingers without harming the man. About 1860, in Grass Valley, California, Lola Montez, an actress, had two well-grown grizzlies which were chained at the front of her cottage. In 1868, Albert E. Kent shot a mother grizzly. He took one of her cubs to his home in Chicago, where it lived in a stable; neither the coachman nor the horses were afraid of the bear. A female cub was kept as a pet at a sawmill, where she roamed about unchained. She left of her own free will in her third summer. Philip A. Rollins raised two grizzly cubs which were not confined but allowed to go and come as they pleased. At the end of four years one of them died from poison. The other, because he resented being teased by a visiting ranchman, was taken many miles from the ranch by the keeper and released. The big bear was back at the ranch eight hours before the return of the man who had released him.

The most famous tame grizzlies of all, however, were those owned by Grizzly Adams, a California hunter, who actually trained two bears to be his constant hunting companions. One of these, "Lady Washington," was taught to be a regular pack animal and with a saddle would carry loads up to two hundred pounds. Another of Adams's grizzlies was "Ben Franklin," who assisted Adams in hunting. In order to show the docility of his bears, Adams would unchain Ben Franklin and ride on his back.

Adams and his bears performed in P. T. Barnum's show in New York City in 1860. On the opening day Adams paraded his animals down Broadway and up the Bowery. Three of his grizzlies rode on a wagon with him, and only two were chained. The third bear, "General Fremont," was not chained and Adams rode on his back.

There is a difference between taming an animal and training it. A gentle horse often becomes violently dangerous when first saddled, and it was evident that some grizzlies resented the harsh training methods used by Adams. In 1855, he was almost scalped by a wounded wild grizzly which he killed. Along with this he received other head injuries and terrific blows from his captive grizzlies while he was training them. The total of all these injuries finally cost him his life, and he died October 25, 1860, at forty-eight years of age.

Many animals respond to sounds because of their highly developed sense of hearing. Birds fly away from a feeder when a door is opened, and dogs are alerted by sounds that may not be audible to man. The grizzly also is responsive to sounds. Holzworth, who studied and photographed grizzlies in Alaska, wrote: "The cabin was on the shore of the creek, and I could see bears fishing from the cabin window. About 2 A.M. I was awakened by splashing and I started, in the dark, for the window. I collided with a large tin pan that was hanging on the wall and when this fell it made quite a noise. Out of the window I saw and heard two bears flying out of the creek and go crashing into the brush on the other side."

Another time Holzworth trained his camera on a bear that had

58

stepped out into the creek only about twenty feet away. The animal took a few steps into the water, heard the whir of the movie camera, and dived back into the brush. Once Holzworth watched every day at a place where bears came to fish for salmon. Not one appeared, however, and he concluded that this was probably because he had thoughtlessly fired several shots from his rifle while trying out the telescopic sight.

L. J. Drummond, a botanist working in the Rockies, said that he often came upon grizzly bears unexpectedly. When he made a noise with his tin specimen box, they would rear up, look at him, and then move off. Willard A. Troyer and his research party in Alaska chased big brown bears away from their trapped cubs by firing rifles, by exploding firecrackers from shotguns, and by having all of the men in the crew shout loudly as they advanced toward the distressed mother bears.

Mr. and Mrs. Arthur Newton Pack, on Admiralty Island, Alaska, experimented in order to discover the reactions of the big brown bears to the strains of the accordion. Mrs. Pack concluded that "there is no musical critic among the bears."

I have played recordings of music to dogs, and so far as I could determine there was no reaction on the part of the animals. Dogs trained to stand on their hind legs and dance to the strains of a waltz do the same thing without music. Also, bears that dance, roller-skate, and ride bicycles are generally trained without music. The circus band and the TV orchestra provide background music for the audience. So it seems that some animals, at least, are not responsive to music.

I once saw a black bear bite off and eat a small portion of another black bear that had been dead for several days and was lying in the forest. However, I have never observed any cannibalistic tendencies in the grizzly, although others have. William H. Wright imparted the following:

On two occasions I have known an old male grizzly to kill and eat a small cub that was tied up with a chain. Once I found this evidence. A female, mother of two cubs, was caught in a trap (steel). And while

59

thus held an old male grizzly came along, and not only killed her, but had killed and eaten the cubs. When we arrived he was sitting under a tree, close by, and we shot him in the head. We found a few scraps of the cubs lying about and part of one of them was buried near where he had been sitting.

Dr. William T. Hornaday claimed that male bears in captivity would be likely to destroy young cubs during their first six months if they got the opportunity. Because of this it was absolutely necessary to separate the father from his family. This tendency also exists in other species of wild and domestic animals.

Holzworth made the general statement that the male bear, whether father or stranger, is cannibalistic; he would probably kill the cubs and eat them. This same writer also contended that if, during a fight, one bear kills another, the victor usually turns cannibal and eats his antagonist. Neither of these two statements is substantiated by definitive examples.

Spring

IN THE WORLD OF NATURE, spring is the time when new life is born. It is the wakening moon of the Indian and the love moon for many animals. For the woodchuck it is the time for mating and breeding, but not for the grizzly bear.

In midwinter, alone in her snow-covered lair, the female grizzly knows the pain and possibly the joy of motherhood. The time is January or February, and the winter den, usually at a high elevation, may be blanketed with more than six feet of snow. The nursery, which was dug by the mother herself, is snug and roomy, but this matters little to the newborn cubs, for they are tiny, blind, deaf, toothless, and helpless.

The fertilized ova of the grizzly show little or no growth prior to the winter sleep. After mating, development of the embryo starts, then ceases for a time, and is later resumed. This phenomenon is known as *delayed implantation*. In its early stage the embryo remains essentially free in the uterus of the female; then it becomes implanted and growth proceeds. This is known to be true of the black bear as well as of the grizzly bear.

A 120-pound human mother may give birth to a 6- or even an 8-pound infant. Not so with the grizzly, however. The mother bear, whether 400 pounds or 800 pounds, gives birth to cubs that weigh only about 1½ pounds each. This infant weight may vary slightly, but the size of the mother has no effect upon the size and weight of the cubs.

Two Kodiak bear cubs were born in the Cleveland Zoological Park

A baby porcupine weighs about 1 pound, while the mother may be only 15 pounds. Grizzly babies weigh about 1½ pounds at birth; the mother may weigh 500 pounds.

on February 7. At birth the male weighed 20 ounces and the female 24 ounces. When one month old the male weighed 37 ounces and the female, 47 ounces. At the age of two months the male had increased to 52 ounces and the female was 64 ounces. When three months of age the male was 5½ pounds and the female an even 6 pounds.

In the Bronx Zoo, New York City, a single grizzly cub, born January 13, weighed 18 ounces. Another infant, a female, born January 17 in the Central Park Zoo, New York City, was 8½ inches in length and weighed 24 ounces. It seems then that the weight of a grizzly cub may vary somewhat, even as does the weight of a human baby. This size variation, however, does not alter the fact that, by comparison with their giant mother, infant grizzlies are tiny and may be only about 1/600 of their mother's weight.

Recorded dates of the births of grizzlies in captivity are January 9, 11, 13, 15, 17, 18, and February 7. Ernest Thompson Seton described a female cub that was born in captivity on January 17:

It weighs 1½ pounds, is 8½ inches long from tip of tail to end of nose. It is blind and will continue so for 9 or 10 days. It is apparently naked, but covered with a very fine, short gray hair, and [the skin] is of pale pink or flesh tint. The ears are low and the openings not yet visible. It squeals like a child when it is hungry, and is very restless, nosing about, falling on its back, and screaming in temper.

The little one had all the form of a Grizzly—the shape of head, the hump on shoulders, the paws and lower jaw.

Ralph S. Palmer wrote that the cubs have a whine and a purring hum and the Craigheads stated that when grizzly cubs nurse they make a buzzing sound like a swarm of bees.

It seems probable that at times the mother carries her babies, possibly when they wander away to inspect their dark home. I have seen a gray squirrel carry her baby by holding the skin of its belly in her mouth while the infant curled its body around the head of its mother. Dogs and cats carry their offspring by the nape of the neck. However, few have seen how a grizzly carries its young. The only record I have of this procedure is a photograph of a big brown bear in the Whipsnade Zoo, London. There the animals roam about in the open, enclosed only by ditches. This mother bear carried her very small cub by holding the infant's head in her mouth and allowing its body to dangle.

All animals are not blind when born. The eyes of the white-tailed deer's fawn and those of the moose calf are open and bright at birth. This is very reasonable because these youngsters are capable of walking almost at once.

The infant grizzly, though, is born in the darkness of its mother's winter den where sight would be useless. So the fact that its eyes do not open for nine or ten days is of no importance. However this is quite different from black bear cubs, whose eyes remain closed until they are about forty days old.

Why are bear cubs so small? A 130-pound whitetail doe may give birth to twin fawns weighing 4 pounds each, and a moose calf weighs 20 to 25 pounds the instant that it is born. Twin grizzly cubs weigh a total of only 3 pounds, which is less than the weight of one whitetail fawn. However, the fawn can and does stand up ten minutes after birth, and it can walk when about one hour old. Infant grizzlies remain in their nursery for three or four months, and during this time their only nourishment is the mother's milk. The mother, also confined to her winter lair, gets no food at all. If her babies were big, the drain on her milk supply would be too great. Grizzly Adams wrote that cubs generally cut their teeth in about two months, but they do not have a full set until maturity. The mother should be grateful for this, because sharp, pointed milk teeth can be very annoying on tender nipples.

I have seen a number of mother grizzlies with two young, but only once have I come upon a female with three and another with four cubs. Others agree with my observations, and Hubbard reported families of two and three young but only one female with quadruplets. In his opinion two is the usual number of offspring.

Mother grizzly with two cubs.

Seton wrote that a female grizzly in a zoological park produced a total of twenty-two cubs in twelve litters, or an average of just under two cubs per litter. A. H. Macpherson wrote: "The average in Canadian national parks is close to two, and the mean of fourteen litters of cubs and yearlings sighted in the Northwest Territories was also two."

In an aerial survey of grizzlies in Alaska in August, 1966, Jack W. Lentfer noted that 2.19 cubs was the average number per litter. No mothers with four young were seen, and females with two and three cubs predominated.

Frank and John Craighead estimated that the average size of a litter is 2.2 cubs. Triplets are born frequently, and the largest litter recorded was four. In the Craigheads' opinion the annual birth rate of the total grizzly population in Yellowstone National Park averages about 20 per cent, and this is slightly higher than the death rate. They have found that, among cubs, males outnumber females two to one. At three to four years of age the sexes are about equal; among the adults, females predominate.

In the human white population of the United States, according to the Bureau of the Census, males only slightly outnumber females under one year of age (less than 1 per cent). At three to four years of age there is little change, but after fourteen years the females outnumber the males and continue to do so thereafter. The white man in this country is essentially monogamous and the sex ratio is of no significance biologically. However, many wild animals are polygamous. A bull elk, for example, has a harem, and one male can serve a number of females. Likewise, the male bear, or boar, as he is called, is capable of mating with more than one female so that the race may be perpetuated. Therefore, the sex balance does not necessarily alter the breeding of the grizzly, and no social laws prohibit promiscuity. In fact the Craigheads noted that the annual crop of cubs in Yellowstone National Park is sired by only a few large, aggressive males.

It is April or May when the cubs first emerge from their nursery den, although the exact time may depend upon the locality. T. W. Barry saw a female and two cubs emerge on May 24, near Liverpool Bay, Canada, and another on May 10, near the mouth of the Kugaluk River, Canada. On the Alaska Peninsula, Lentfer observed a mother and three cubs leave their den on May 25.

When for the first time they leave the den in which they were born, the cubs are fully furred, bright-eyed, and about four months old. They are usually gray, with dark ears and feet and a dark patch around each eye. At this time they weigh about 5 to 7 pounds. A male cub in the Cleveland Zoo weighed 5½ pounds and his sister was 6 pounds when they were three months old.

All winter the baby bears suckle, so that their diet has been strictly milk. Seton believed that they "begin to eat solid food as soon as they can get it; that is, after they have begun active life in the spring." Writing of captive bears, Hornaday stated: "I think that the average age at which grizzly cubs feed independently of mother's milk is about 4 months. The beginning on solid food is made very slowly and the youngsters nurse vigorously all summer." In the wild this is necessary, for in grizzly bear land the earth is generally snow-covered, and there is little or no vegetable food for the bears when they first leave their winter den.

I have personally observed cubs suckle during the summer months and in the last week of August. At this time, however, they were also eating solid food. During salmon fishing time in Alaska, the cubs eat fish which the mother catches for them. These fish begin to enter the fresh-water streams to spawn during the latter part of June and continue for some time thereafter.

It has been pointed out that the grizzly cub grows somewhat more slowly than the black bear cub, both in size and in self-reliance. I have found this to be true and I have noted, in midsummer, examples of black bear cubs that were one quarter or one third larger than the grizzly cubs I was observing. It was also evident that the young black bears were more adventurous than their grizzly cousins. They often wandered away

66

Grizzly cubs about seven months old. These two were eating solid food and also suckling.

Black bear cubs often wander away from their mother. These two were alone but the female was probably in the vicinity.

from their mothers when playing and when investigating their new world. But the grizzlies remained with their parent and seemed ready and willing to do her bidding.

This relative freedom of the black bear cubs may be owing to the fact that the mother black bear often leaves her cubs in a tree, apparently with strict orders to them to remain there until she returns. A number of times I have discovered black bear cubs bawling loudly from a tree top in which their mothers had left them. I have also seen black bear cubs roaming about without their parent, although she was probably nearby. However, I have never come upon grizzly cubs that were not with their mother. Because her children are not tree climbers, she does not leave them, and grizzly mothers are willing and capable of defending their young against other animals, including male grizzlies.

Grizzly cubs do not wander away from their mother. This mother grizzly is watching an advancing male grizzly, which she chased away from her cubs.

Spring

I once saw a large silvertip make his way toward a female and her twins. The mother advanced to a position between the big male and her cubs and when the advancing bear was about thirty feet away she charged. There was no fight, because the male turned and ran away. Possibly his retreat was an act of chivalry.

The mother, though, has no defense against man and his rifle. However brave, she cannot win, but certainly she tries and usually dies because of her valor. Grizzly Adams once shot and killed a mother bear, but her two yearling cubs escaped. After a few days Adams and his comrades returned to the scene and found the cubs clinging to the dead body of the mother.

This same Grizzly Adams had, in his own harsh way, a deep appreciation of nature and a certain fondness for animals. However, he had no scruples about slaughter, for he was first of all a hunter. One day he watched a grizzly playing with two cubs in a pool. These are his own words:

I looked for a considerable time upon the scene, and did not fire till she appeared about ready to withdraw, when, as it happened, I merely broke her shoulder. She rushed for me at once, but I seized my rifle by the barrel and struck her over the head, and then jumped to the bed of the creek and drew my knife, with which I dealt her a stab in the flank. As I struck, she reared up and bore me to the ground; and, while she placed her paw upon my head, bit me severely in the shoulder, the marks of which I still bear. I lay perfectly still, however, and in a few minutes the cubs began bawling, when the old Bear, seeing no resistance in me, turned to them. Seizing this opportunity, I sprang to my feet again and drew my pistol; but, observing at a glance that the stab in the flank was fatal, I did not fire. The poor brute was evidently dying, although she tried to pacify her cubs. Although I stood but a few yards distant, she had not the strength to come at me; for she had bled, and was still bleeding profusely. As I watched her licking her young and giving them her last attentions, as if conscious of the approach of death, I thought there was something of the human in the Bear, and was sorry I had shot so affectionate a mother.

69

A less grim story concerns a cub which was captured and transported on horseback seven or eight miles to the ranch of Fred Alispaw in Colorado. A heavy collar was placed about the cub's neck and a chain fastened to it. Then the youngster was pushed into an old cage and the chain passed through the bars and secured to a stout post outside of the cage. That night the mother bear paid the ranch a visit, whipped a whole pack of dogs, tore the cage to bits, broke the chain, and led her cub away. Neither of them was ever seen again.

When grizzlies retire to their winter dens they are fat and well-furred. When they emerge in the spring they are still fat and well-furred because their long, deep sleep does not draw significantly upon their supply of

When they emerge in the spring, grizzlies are still fat and in good physical condition.

Loss of weight occurs after they have left their winter quarters, because at this time food is scarce.

fat and energy. It is after leaving their winter lair that the bears suffer a loss of weight, because food is very scarce at this time. They eat sparingly the first week or ten days after coming forth, and then they begin to feed on shoots of grass, skunk cabbage, and similar foods, plus the carcasses of winter-killed animals.

William Wells observed that when the grizzly emerges from its winter den "he is still hog-fat. At first he does not go far from his den but after a few days he starts for the side hills, where the snowslides have swept the snow away. Here he can get a few mouthfuls of grass."

The male bear does not den with the female and he does nothing to protect his family or to provide for them. In fact, males may be deadly foes of cubs, and a male bear, whether father or stranger, will probably kill the cubs if an opportunity is afforded. Dr. Hornaday, of the Bronx Zoo, has already been noted as saying that in captivity it is absolutely necessary to separate the father from his family because the male would very likely kill the cubs. However, the attitude of different male bears toward their offspring may vary. In Golden Gate Park, San Francisco, the little ones sometimes put their paws through the cage to their father. He would sniff at the paws very loudly and utter a sort of quick, short "Koff, koff, koff, koff." It was not a menace, as he offered them no harm, though he had ample opportunity.

It is no reflection upon the character of the grizzly that the male, according to our standards, is a poor father. Males of other species are in the same category. The buck deer, the bull moose, and the male woodchuck are but a few of the mammals that abandon their mates and young and do not participate in family care. This may be because these three species are plant-eaters. With the flesh-eating red fox it is different. The male fox hunts and carries food to his mate while she remains at home with her suckling pups. Both parents take food to their offspring when they are old enough to eat it. Furthermore, both mother and father participate in their family's education and through united efforts teach their pups to hunt for food. Apparently these are adaptations to the

71

Father woodchuck does nothing to help the mother rear her young.

survival of each species, brought about through millions of years of evolution, and both the grizzly and the red fox father do as they do without ever knowing why.

I have observed that the mother grizzly is a tender and devoted parent. I have never seen a grizzly bear cuff her young. There always seems to be perfect understanding between mother and child, and every grizzly cub I have seen was strictly obedient.

Undoubtedly there is a means of communication between bears, regardless of age, and the young respond to the will of the mother. Holzworth confirmed this and wrote: "We saw two large black grizzly cubs appear, not over fifteen yards away. They had given us about ten feet of film when the wary old mother appeared and woofed an immediate retreat."

In the San Francisco Zoo the mother often uttered a sort of choppy, coughing sound to her three-month-old cubs. She seemed always quite concerned for them and once, during a sudden heavy rain, she swept the two young under her huge body. Then, straddling very wide, she sheltered them from the rain and guided them back into the den.

The cubs are born without fear, and must be taught to be afraid; this emotion is not a product of instinct but a very important factor for survival. It seems then that wise and experienced mothers are the best teachers, and this may be so.

One method of teaching is by doing, for youngsters are very apt to mimic. The mother may turn over stones to search for insects, and soon the cubs will turn over stones also. Ernest Thompson Seton quoted Dr. J. C. Merrill, who watched a silvertip and her cubs for more than a week in the Bighorn Mountains and who stated:

The chief occupation of the Bears while in sight was turning over stones in search of insects beneath.

The habit of turning over stones is very general in the spring and early summer. This family of bears were regular in their habits, feeding from early morning till about 9 o'clock, and reappearing about 4 in the afternoon.

These cubs were undoubtedly being taught and may have, at first, been mimicking their mother.

Writing of bears fishing for salmon in Alaska, Robert L. Usinger not-

Cubs are born without fear and must be taught to recognize danger.

ed: "The cubs are too young to fend for themselves during their first summer, but the following year their mothers lead them to the streams and instruct them in the art of fishing."

Spring is from about March 21 to June 21, and aside from winter, when the grizzly sleeps, this is the most inactive season. If the bears emerge in May there is only a month or so of spring remaining, and the snow-bound western highlands restrict their activities. Although they may not know it, the big bears are waiting for summer rains, fresh green plantlife and an abundance of food, and warm sunshine.

Summer

SUMMER IS THE SEASON when pleasant and important things happen in the world of the grizzly bear. The time of hunger is past, and the time of deep snow and freezing weather is months ahead. This is the season of growth and learning and experience for the young and the time for courting and mating for the grownups. The female grizzly mates only every two or three years, and she and her offspring remain together as a family unit until the cubs are yearlings or two-year-olds. During this time the female does not tolerate amorous advances of males.

The season of mating begins slowly, in late May, but it is at its peak from mid-June to mid-July. This time may be extended, though, because females continue to be in heat until they are bred. Knowledge of the

This is a mother grizzly with her two-year-old cubs. The young are nearly as big as their mother.

This larger male and the smaller female are mates. The mating season is at its peak from mid-June to mid-July.

mating activities of the grizzly has been accumulated by many observers. In Mount McKinley Park, Alaska, copulation was observed on June 16, 1957, by Neil J. Reed, Park Naturalist. K. R. D. Mundy saw a pair copulating on June 19, 1962, in Glacier National Park, British Columbia. Lewis and Clark recorded bears having sexual intercourse on June 15. In Golden Gate Park, San Francisco, the act of mating was on June 19, and in the Central Park Zoo, New York, a pair mated in July. In Colorado, Thomas Drummond saw a male caressing a female in late June.

It was in July when one of Grizzly Adams' female bears had her first romance. She was then perhaps four years old. Adams and his party were camped not far from Salt Lake City, when they learned that the she-bear was being visited nightly by an amorous male. Adams, the rugged mountaineer, forbade his men to shoot the visitor, and in due time his pet became the mother of a cub which grew up to be another of his tame grizzly bears.

The midsummer courtship may last a month or more, during which time the pair feed, play, and wrestle together. Then they separate and lead solitary lives. Although they may remain together during love-making, the fidelity of the mighty grizzly may be questioned. Black bears, according to Joe Van Wormer, are considered to be monogamous on a year-to-year basis; that is, a mated pair are faithful during their brief one-month summer "marriage," but afterward they separate. Not so with the grizzly. If another male intrudes, the female is likely to run away from him. If he is powerful enough and very persistent, he may finally be allowed to share the female's favor. This situation is somewhat similar to the courting of domestic dogs. A number of male dogs, even of different breeds, may follow, annoy, and copulate with the same female. Frank and John Craighead assure us that, in grizzlies, both sexes are promiscuous.

It is social law and not biological law that imposes monogamy upon man, when it is practiced. Some other animals, such as foxes, are monogamous and some are not. The males of a species of mammal in which the fathers do not assist in feeding and caring for the young are very apt to be promiscuous. Without family duties they are free to serve a number of different females. This may actually be an important factor in sustaining the population of that species. The bull elk, for example, collects a harem and fights off other bulls which strive to seduce his mates. The strongest animal wins and is privileged to be the father of the next generation of elk. In this way weak and sickly males are prevented from mating, and the possibilities of a healthy herd are greatly enhanced.

The elk is polygamous. The bull collects a harem and mates with a number of females.

The World of the Grizzly Bear

All animals pass through various stages of growth and development. Sexual maturity is the time when the animal is capable of successfully mating and breeding. The grizzly bear reaches sexual maturity when three to five years of age. In a study in northwestern Wyoming, females bred first when about three and a half years old, and then every second or third year. A female tamed by Grizzly Adams mated first when about four years old. Albert W. Erickson stated that records of captives indicate that both sexes attain puberty at approximately three and a half years.

It might not be amiss to mention here that in captivity a big brown bear mated with a female polar bear, and the polar bear gave birth to offspring after a gestation period of 180 days. This is surprising because the grizzly and the polar bear are thought by taxonomists to be so different that scientists have not classified them even in the same genus.

Based upon this known mating of bears in captivity, the gestation period of the grizzly is about 180 days. A female in the Central Park Zoo, New York, gave birth to young 184 days after mating. Another female in the Golden Gate Park, San Francisco, had the same period of gestation, 184 days. This seems to be just about right when the time of mating and the time of breeding is used to estimate the gestation period. Assuming that conception occurred July 1, at the height of the mating season, and that the cubs were born February 1, the period of gestation would be 184 days, and this agrees with established records.

It is generally conceded that no species of animal other than man has ever been known to carry on wholesale destruction of itself. Many of the same kind of animals fight among themselves, but this is, usually, individually, and for some definite reason. Grizzly bears may fight over their territories and their mates. Or they may fight over food and in defense of their young. Holzworth in Alaska, who heard the big brown bears fighting at night on beaches and river flats, wrote: "Once I heard a fight that lasted over two hours on a beach, while I was anchored in a small boat. When I went ashore the next day the ground around the place was torn up and there was hair and blood on the ground." To this,

This is a young sexually mature grizzly. This stage is reached at three to five years of age.

Hubbard added: "I have seen several grizzly battle grounds. Each of the fights took place in June, July or August, the grizzlys' mating season."

Frank and John Craighead gave a blow by blow description of a fight they witnessed:

What a battle! Inge [one of the bears] rushed his adversary and sank his canines deep into 88's [the other contestant's] rump. The momentum carried him over his opponent. But Inge recovered, seized 88's right thigh, and shook the 700-pound boar as a terrier shakes a rat.

Eighty-eight broke away, and his huge jaws clamped on Inge's jowls. The boss bear roared, reared back to full height, and fought free. A great red gash marred his face.

The two stood on hind legs, face to face, jaws agape, parrying like monstrous boxers. Then they locked jaws, each levering to throw the other to the ground. Inge slapped his adversary across the shoulder with a lightning-fast swipe from his right paw, then lunged for 88's throat.

79

Eighty-eight staggered back, now bleeding from several deep wounds, but gave bite for bite and blow for blow. The combatants' roars could be heard half a mile away.

Both silvertips dropped to all fours. Then 88 bowed his head and looked aside. Inge read this sign of submission and deliberately turned his back, moving to claim his sow. . . . The contest was over. Inge remained supreme.

Once I was fortunate in seeing a battle between two wild black bears. They did not bite but stood up on their hind legs and delivered crushing right and left blows to each other's bodies. Bears cannot close their fists, so the blows were swiping slaps that might have crushed the ribs and broken the back of a man. There was no ducking or blocking the blows, and the sound when they landed was like that of a baseball bat striking a leather cushion. During the fight both bears continued to utter loud, bawling blats and growls. I worked in to about a hundred feet and took a picture but it seemed unwise to venture any closer.

I also saw a fight between two grizzly bears that came to my bait early one evening. One, which was eating, growled when the other approached, and the two stood on all four feet, face to face. Then they attempted to bite, but each evaded the other's jaws at first. After this preliminary, they began in earnest, and I saw fur ripped from the neck and throat of both bears. They were growling loudly now, and one got hold of the other's ear. It gave a quick shake and then tried for the side of the neck. The other bear turned away, and it was evident that an understanding had been reached. The fight was over, and only the winner returned to the food.

This battle lasted only a minute or two, but during this time neither contestant reared up on its hind legs and neither bear slapped the other with its forepaws as did the black bears.

The grizzly has all the equipment necessary to be a meat-eating animal, and that is what it is. Because of its sharp sturdy teeth it has been classified as a carnivore or flesh-eater, but it does not limit its diet

Beginning of a fight. One approached while the other was eating.

to meat. The grizzly is omnivorous, and will eat practically anything that is edible, whether plant or animal.

The feeding habits of any creature may be directly responsible for man's attitude toward it. If the animal feeds on what man needs or wants, it is said to be injurious and may be sentenced to be killed on sight. In the early 1880's, when domestic cattle were turned loose on the grizzly's range, the big bear was condemned as a stock killer, and this was a contributing factor in its destruction. Cattlemen and sheepmen offered rewards for its death, and as late as 1860 a bounty of ten dollars

81

was given by the State of California for each grizzly scalp. The opinion of these early Americans was, however, not based upon facts.

Enos A. Mills studied the alleged killing of cattle by grizzlies, and presented evidence that acquitted the grizzly. He reported:

I have investigated more than 14 cases in which the grizzly was charged with killing cattle. In a number of instances there was not a trace of a grizzly near the carcass. There were traces of other animals, but the guilty one could not be determined. There were eleven carcasses that had been visited by grizzlies; six of these animals had been killed by mountain lions, one by poisonous plants, one by wolves, two by stones that rolled from a land-slip. In the eleventh case neither the carcass nor its surroundings gave any conclusive evidence for determining the cause of the cow's death. The carcass had been fed upon by coyotes, wolves, lions, and both black and grizzly bears. In all of these cases the only evidence against the grizzly was entirely circumstantial; he had eaten a part of the carcass.

I was once trailing a grizzly through the snow, when he came upon the trail of a mountain lion, which he followed. Farther along the lion killed a horse. When the grizzly came upon the scene, he drove the lion off. The following day, while having a second feast off the horse, he was discovered by a rancher, who at once procured dogs and pursued and killed the famous horse-killing grizzly.

Cattle-killing is not a race habit of grizzlies, but some individuals do now and then turn to cattle, like the tiger that turns man-eater. A number of bears have been regarded as stock-killing outlaws; following are a few from the list of those that became famous:

The Butcher, or simply Butch. Wyoming, 1896–1900. Blamed for killing livestock valued at $4,500. Bounty offer of $375 was never collected. Bear disappeared in the fall of 1900 and was not seen again.

Old Mose. Black Mountains near Canyon City, Colorado, 1882–1904. Said to have killed thousands of dollars' worth of cattle. Weighed 875 pounds, hog dressed. Skin measured 10 feet 4 inches long and 9 feet

6 inches across the shoulders. Had a price of $100 on his head.

Old Roughhouse. Primarily a sheep killer. Killed by a sheepherder in Montana, 1901.

Two Toes. In 1898, a trapper named Ricks caught a Montana grizzly in a steel trap. The animal tore itself free but left part of its paw in the trap. The bear turned stock killer and because of its maimed foot was known as Two Toes. It could always be identified by its track, and during its career, 1902–1906, it killed an estimated $8,750 in livestock. The bear, a male, was taken by a man named Dale, who collected $575 reward from cattlemen.

Bloody Paws. Among the outlaw grizzlies, Bloody Paws seems to hold the record for the number of domestic animals killed. During three years, 1889–1892, she was said to have killed 570 head of domestic animals. An Indian, Buffalo Robe, killed her and collected the $375 bounty.

Whether or not these famous grizzly outlaws were guilty of all the killings for which they were blamed will never be known. I doubt it, and my doubt is based upon recent personal experiences. For example, a farmer told me a red fox had killed two hundred of his chickens in one week. He finally admitted to me that about thirty-five chickens had been killed, and he was not sure that the red fox was the culprit. It might have been dogs. Another man reported that thirty-five acres of woodlot had been flooded by beavers. I paced off the flooded area and estimated about five acres were inundated.

In studies of bears in Alaska in 1966, research workers examined 66 cattle and 2 horses that had died on the range. It was determined that one Angus calf had been killed by bears on October 26. Another calf had been shot. Some mortalities were attributed to disease associated with starvation. Other dead animals reported by ranchers included 80 winter killed, 3 shot by hunters or vandals, and 5 which might have been killed by bears. Of the total of 156, one animal was definitely believed to have been killed by bears, and five others *might* have been slain by grizzlies.

Seton reported a killer grizzly that lived in the Okanogan Forest Reserve, Washington:

This Bear, a Grizzly, had been responsible for heavy losses during the past three years, and was definitely known to have killed 35 head of Cattle and 150 head of Sheep during the summer of 1923. The latter part of July [1924] it appeared near a camp after dusk and attacked a 4-year-old steer. Hearing the noise, the camp foreman investigated and found the Grizzly holding the steer with its fore feet and biting at its neck. A shot failed to take any effect and the Bear ran away. At the request of livestock owners, an experienced hunter with trained Dogs was assigned to the task and effected the capture of this notorious animal in about three weeks. This Bear weighed over 1,100 pounds.

Note that no data are presented to prove that the cattle and sheep were definitely killed by this grizzly. There is a great difference between proof, mere circumstantial evidence, and the opinions of prejudiced persons. Summer is three months or ninety-two days long, and if this bear had killed a total of 185 domesticated animals, as charged, it would have slain two animals each day. Based upon the opinions of those who know the bear, this is absurd and supports the statements of experts who contend that the depredations of the grizzly have been greatly exaggerated.

The grizzly was also said to have been a threat to the buffalo. It has been stated that a grizzly would often follow a herd of these shaggy beasts and pull down an aged or sickly animal when it lagged behind. This was a known practice of wolves but not of grizzlies. It is now generally agreed that most of such killings were done by wolves, though the grizzly was often blamed for them.

According to early accounts, when bear and bulls were put into an arena, the grizzly was reluctant to fight. This suggests that the bear was also probably reluctant to attack range cattle and therefore did not generally kill and feed upon domestic stock and buffalo. One way in which the bear feasted on the buffalo was described by Lewis and Clark: "In the vicinity of the Great Falls of the Missouri, great herds came

Buffalo bulls, which weigh 2,000 pounds or more, are not attacked and killed by grizzlies.

daily to drink. The press of the oncoming buffalo often forced the leaders into the current. Many were swept over the falls. The dead drifted ashore, providing a banquet for the grizzly bears gathered there."

Incidentally a big bull buffalo may weigh 2,000 pounds, while a big grizzly is only half that weight. Also, the buffalo had the backing of hundreds or even thousands of others in the herd. It would seem as though no grizzly would cope with those odds.

Many observations indicate that the grizzly does not hunt for wild game. It does feed upon dead animals, but it generally declines to do its own killing. Seton wrote: "Deer and Buffalo in the form of carrion, he always did eat, but the creatures themselves he did not kill because he could not catch them. The Bears, Black and Grizzly, can scarcely be a menace to Elk, excepting to the calf when it is less than a week old."

So the grizzly may be dangerous to sick or crippled elk, moose, or deer, and also to calves and fawns, but very few records are available to substantiate this possibility. In fact, the grizzly's stomach is often filled only with grass and other vegetation. However, Holzworth in his Alaskan studies found undeniable proof that in one case a grizzly did eat a fawn because he discovered remains in the droppings of a bear—small, non-digestible hoofs that had passed through the bear's intestines.

In Glacier Park, Tom Dawson saw a grizzly trying to catch a mountain goat kid. The white mother goat looked on with little concern from a safe distance, and it seemed she must have known the bear's efforts would be in vain. The huge bear followed the kid, which turned and faced its pursuer. When the grizzly rushed in, the young goat merely turned and bounded up the nearly straight cliff toward its mother and the bear gave up the chase.

All bear and goat encounters, though, do not end in this harmless way. In British Columbia, Arthur B. Fenwick found a large mountain goat lying dead at the spot where it had been killed by a silvertip. Tracks of the bear led away to the place where it, too, lay dead. The nine-inch-long daggerlike horns of the white goat had punctured the bear twice just back of the heart.

It seems as if wild animals do not suffer shock or emotional disturbance because of a close call with sudden death. I have seen birds at my feeders, after they had escaped from the pounce of a cat, fly to the top of the fence above the marauder and preen their feathers. My friend Robert G. Stewart watched a gray squirrel hop toward his feeding station. Suddenly a cat sprang from under a spruce tree and knocked the squirrel over. The two grappled. The gray squirrel tore loose, scurried up a tree to the feeding bench, and with absolutely no sign of concern proceeded to eat its breakfast.

Some very interesting information on the feeding habits of the grizzly bear was given by William H. Wright. In the Bitterroot Mountains of Idaho, this hunter-naturalist observed that the bear in early spring ate

Very young elk calves, if found by a grizzly, may be killed and eaten. When they become fleet-footed, the bear cannot catch them.

Newly born whitetail fawns might also be added to the grizzly's list of food.

Grizzly bears cannot catch the larger game animals, so this cow and calf moose are quite safe.

tender shoots of grass. Later it fed upon fish and then ants, grubs and other insect larvae. When berries were ripe, it ate them in great quantities, and during the autumn run of salmon, the great bear gorged itself on this fine fish.

Wright then added:

Let us turn now to northern Wyoming, a few hundred miles away. Here the grizzly does not dig to any extent for roots, nor is he a confirmed grass and fish eater as he is in the Bitterroots. Aside from the berries that all grizzlies love, and the ants and grubs that they never refuse, he is, spring and fall, decidedly carnivorous. In the Wyoming region there are thousands of head of elk and other game. During the winter many may perish, and their bodies lie until spring under the snow. During the fall many are shot and their carcasses left lying where they fell. These the grizzly feeds on.

In the Bitterroot, strange as it may appear, not one grizzly in 50 would touch a carcass thus found. Farther north in British Columbia, it is again true that not one grizzly in a hundred will touch flesh. In these regions the grizzly lives and dies a vegetarian. They do, however, spend much time in the late fall hunting for and digging out of hibernation Columbian ground squirrels and whistling marmots.

I should say that the reason for some bears not eating meat is because they have never known the taste of it. Where game is plentiful bears have been accustomed to live for part of the time on flesh, and will eat it whenever found.

How can the feeding habits of the grizzly be described precisely when it devours practically anything that is edible, whether it is plant or animal? In spring, young green shoots appear, and these the bear eats because there is nothing else. If fortunate, the hungry giant may find the carcass of a winter-killed elk or deer. Later, other palatable plants provide nourishment, and after that insects and their larvae are eaten by grizzlies. Then, in some parts of the bear's range, the salmon runs begin and at about the same time luscious berries are available. Fungi and mushrooms come forth, and in the autumn the grizzlies dig out

Eating a fish on the bank of a small stream.

hibernating ground squirrels and marmots.

In the opinion of some naturalists, fishes are the food that the grizzly likes best, and from June to October great numbers of salmon ascend the Alaskan and Canadian rivers. However, salmon fishing by bears is not restricted to these northern areas. In the early days grizzlies caught this fine fish in the streams of the western United States just as they do now in the northland. William H. Wright, who watched grizzlies fishing in August and September in streams that were tributary to the Clearwater River in Idaho, once saw five big grizzlies fishing from one log jam and mentioned that their finny prey were two to four feet long.

For many years it was generally believed that the grizzly hooks salmon out of the stream with a quick, skillful sweep of its long-clawed paw, and many illustrators have made drawings and paintings of grizzly bears fishing in this way. This is not true. The bear catches the fish in its mouth and carries the wriggling creature to the shore. Never have I seen a grizzly sweep a fish from the water with its paw, and other observers agree. Some forty years ago John M. Holzworth showed his movies of

89

Alaskan grizzlies at the annual meeting of the American Society of Mammalogists. These pictures revealed big bears capturing salmon in their mouths, and Holzworth told me that they always caught fishes in this way. In *Nature Magazine,* January, 1943, three different photographs showed a bear, in midstream, with salmon that it had just caught held in its powerful jaws. More recently the wild animal photographer, Cleveland Grant, showed movies of grizzlies catching salmon, and every one captured the fish in its mouth.

The salmon is highly prized by the big bear, and it is also a very important food fish for man. Its life begins in the cold water of tributary streams, sometimes hundreds of miles inland. A few months after they hatch, the young journey leisurely downstream. By the time they are about five inches long, they reach the mouth of the river and enter the sea.

For the next four or five years, the salmon swims about, hundreds of miles offshore in the North Pacific. When they become sexually mature they head toward shore, seek their ancestral rivers, and begin their journey up the fresh-water streams to spawn. Experiments with marked fish indicate that each salmon finally makes its way to the stream in which it was born, and, after spawning, the adults drift listlessly downstream and soon die. It is at spawning time that the grizzlies go to their favorite streams to feast.

Eagles, ravens, and crows also feed upon the salmon, and glaucus-winged herring gulls eat the dead fish that are washed ashore or left there by the grizzly bears.

When photographing grizzlies I used meat as bait to lure them. The smell of canned dog food attracted the bears but they did not eat it. They ate canned salmon, but they ignored honey and Karo syrup, although these sweets greatly appeal to black bears. I once saw a grizzly eat a snake, but I do not know if the bear killed it or found the creature dead. I have also seen them eat dead fishes that were on the shore, and I have watched them dig out rodents. A number of bears that I observed

Ravens and sea gulls also eat salmon. Here, they fed upon the photo bait I placed for bears.

were turning over stones in search of insects and their larvae. I never noticed exactly how the bears did this, but Dr. J. C. Merrill painted a vivid word picture of it. He wrote: "A man turning over a stone usually draws it over directly toward himself, to the imminent danger of his toes; but a Bear knows better than that. In the case of a heavy stone, they would brace themselves with one fore leg and with the other raise the stone and give it an outward sweep well to one side, so that it would not strike them when falling."

The World of the Grizzly Bear

In Alaska the grizzly eats dead codfish and giant spider crabs that wash ashore and also the carcasses of seals, sea lions, and even whales that are beached. They also relish cambium, the inner bark of trees, and the seeds of the white-bark pine tree. A. H. MacPherson pointed out that the bear might be destructive to waterfowl in the deltas of the Mackenzie and Anderson rivers in Canada. "One year," he wrote, "about 37 per cent of the snow goose and black brant nests were destroyed, though a portion of the losses was caused by gulls and jaegers."

Because of the wide variety of the grizzly's food, a complete listing of it is not practical, or necessary as *some* items are far more important to it than others.

Healthy adult large animals are seldom, if ever, killed and devoured by the grizzly. It feeds mostly upon large animals that it finds dead; and these may be winter- or hunter-killed. Some of its animal food is:

Deer	Gophers
Elk	Field mice
Caribou	Marmots
Moose	Beavers
Bighorn sheep	Lizards
Mountain goats	Snakes
Cattle	Frogs
Colts	Fishes
Pigs	Bees
Sheep	Grasshoppers
Whales	Ants
Seals	Grubs of insects
Sea lions	Insects and larvae
Ground squirrels	Crabs

The grizzly's plant food includes:

Grass	Salmonberries

92

Summer

Wild oats	Serviceberries
Wheat	Huckleberries
Corn	Wild plums
Clover	Wild cherries
Alfilaria	Grapes
Roots	Nuts
Cow parsnips	Acorns
Horsetail	Mushrooms
Bulbs	Aspen leaves
Dogwood berries	Aspen twigs
Elderberries	Alder bark
Gooseberries	Cinquefoil
Manzanita berries	Liquorice
Blueberries	Seeds of evergreens
Crowberries	Cambium

Probably the last food that the grizzly obtains before denning up for the winter is the marmot, or whistler, and the ground squirrel. When digging out marmots, the bear may excavate a hole eight feet deep and twelve or fifteen feet long.

The ground squirrel is one of the very important items of food for the grizzly.

There seems to be one thing that the grizzly bear will not eat: human flesh. Enos A. Mills pointed this out and stated:

I have not heard of an authentic instance of a grizzly's eating human flesh. Many persons have lost their lives from storms, accidents, and starvation; yet their bodies have lain for days and weeks in territory frequented by grizzlies without being eaten by them. A prospector, his horse, and burro were killed by a falling tree. Grizzlies devoured the bodies of the animals, but that of the prospector was not disturbed. Human flesh appears to be the only thing that a grizzly does not eat.

Some animals store food for winter. Certain species of squirrels and mice hoard seeds and nuts, and the beaver cuts and drags branches of trees to its pond. Meat, however, decomposes, and as far as I know flesh-eating mammals do not store rations for winter.

Caching surplus meat for later meals is practiced by the grizzly, however. After the bear has satisfied its hunger, it covers what is left with sticks, stones, earth, and leaves. It returns again and again to feast until the supply is gone. One morning I found an elk calf that had been killed on a highway. The carcass was fresh, and I transported it to the area where I was working so it could be used as bait for grizzlies during my photography. Late that afternoon, I saw a grizzly pick the calf up and carry it away. I followed carefully and through my binocular saw the bear stop and eat part of the elk. Then it dug a shallow hole, put the calf in, and covered it with earth and branches. The next day I did not see the bear, but on the third evening I saw a coyote begin to dig for the elk calf. The bear must have been hiding nearby because it rushed forth and chased the coyote. It then ate some of the calf and carried the remainder away.

Dr. Hornaday told of finding a cache in which a grizzly had buried a mountain goat:

On the steep hillside a shallow hole had been dug, the whole carcass rolled into it, and then upon it had been piled nearly a wagon-load of fresh earth, moss, and green plants that had been torn up by the roots.

The yellow-bellied marmot and its larger relative, the hoary marmot, are near the top of the list of grizzly food.

Beaver (shown here), mice, and other rodents store food for winter use. The grizzly does not.

Over the highest point of the carcass the mass was twenty-four inches deep. On the ground the cache was elliptical in shape, about seven by nine feet. On the lower side it was four feet high, and the upper side two feet. The pyramid was built around two small larch saplings, as if to secure their support.

On the uphill side of the cache, the ground was torn up in a space shaped like a half-moon, twenty-eight feet long by nineteen feet wide. From this space every green thing had been torn up and piled on the pyramid. The outer surface of the cone was a mass of curly, fibrous roots and fresh earth.

The family life and the mode of living of the mighty grizzly varies with sex, age, season, and locality. For this great bear there is the time to be born, the time to den, to court, and to mate, to grow, to learn, and then the time to pass on, leaving a space for others to fill.

I have seen lone adult grizzlies at various times, and this is usual, because mature males live alone except during the mating period. Adult

A solitary grizzly.

A family group: mother and yearling.

females also live alone except over a period of about two years when rearing their young. Every second or third summer the female normally mates, and so for a month or more she may consort with the male. Then she lives alone for several months until the time when her cubs are born, in January or February.

The family group generally consists only of the mother and her cubs. The youngsters may be only a few months old or they may be more than a year old. I have seen small and very young cubs with their parent and some that were almost as big as she. The larger cubs I estimated to be more than two years old, so that they were in their third summer.

Other grizzlies I have seen were subadults which had recently been abandoned by their mother. Some of these were alone, while others, probably brothers and sisters, were still together. This family break is normal, for the cubs are now self-sustaining. Also, it is again mating time for the female, and now she wants no family interference in her relations with the male.

There is yet another group I have studied and photographed. It is composed of one or two bears, about four years old, that have recently become sexually mature.

Family group: four cubs, sub-adults, about 2½ years old, recently abandoned by the mother, who is now actively mating.

Family group: two young, sexually mature grizzlies who are living together but have not yet mated. They are not brother and sister and will probably mate next summer.

On the Alaska Peninsula, August 16, 1961, Albert W. Erickson watched a mother brown bear fishing for salmon. With her were two yearlings, or possibly two-year-olds, and one small cub of the year. This was his only record of a mixed-age litter, and he has observed more than two thousand bears. Sometimes the grizzly mother will adopt the cubs of another. In one example, when the litters of two females became mixed, one retained both litters.

In the wild, then, an observer may see solitary adult males and females; mothers with cubs; larger subadult cubs, singly, or in groups of two or three; and also young, sexually mature animals alone or in company with another.

I have never seen two families of grizzlies together. Holzworth, however, related that on one occasion two cubs and two old females were together. They were walking along the same path and seemed to be associating. This was the only exception that he saw to the usual rule of families remaining apart from each other.

It is not difficult to identify cubs that are under one year old. When they first leave their nursery den in April or May, they weigh only about 5 to 7 pounds and so they are actually smaller than adult woodchucks. Holzworth reported that, on August 20, "a she-grizzly and a little cub appeared about thirty yards off and gave us about twenty feet of good fishing pictures. The old lady would pounce on a salmon and eat it, while the cub looked on with interest." This youngster did not partake of the fish, but the next day Holzworth saw "a big brown

98

When cubs first leave their den in April or May, they are smaller than adult wood-chucks and weigh only about 5 to 7 pounds.

she-bear with a cunning little cub. They were on a gravel bar which extended for some distance up the creek; both were sitting on their haunches while she was feeding him some fish." In another year these small cubs would have grown considerably and would have learned to fish, although at first they would not be as expert at it as their mothers.

Cubs in August are about seven months old and weigh 20 to 40 pounds. In late October, when ten months old, their weight has increased to from 50 to 80 pounds; a captive at this time was slightly under 80 pounds. Black bear cubs of the same age weigh just about the same as grizzlies. A male pet grizzly cub in August, when it was seven months old,

Cubs in August, when about seven months old, weigh 20 to 40 pounds.

In autumn, black bear cubs of the same age as grizzly cubs weigh about the same.

weighed 60 pounds but his twin sister weighed only 46 pounds.

Yearlings are those cubs that have had one birthday but not two, and they weigh 100 to 200 pounds. At the end of its second summer the weight of a zoo grizzly was 190 pounds.

Bears begin to grow soon after they are born, and they continue to grow until they are eight to ten years old. It is then, and not until then, that they reach their full stature and weight. A five-year-old grizzly may appear full grown, but it will continue to develop in size and weight for some years thereafter. In the National Zoological Park at Washington, D.C., an adult male weighed 730 pounds but a 3½-year-old male weighed only 514 pounds.

Summer is a time of plenty, and it is also weaning time for grizzly bear cubs. When they first emerge from the den in early spring, they are nearly four months old. At this time there is no solid food for them to try their baby teeth on because their world is snowbound. Hornaday found that grizzly cubs in a zoo began to eat solid food when about four months old, and in the wild the cubs are just about this age when the

A full-grown grizzly.

This grizzly, about five years old, has not attained full growth. In the field these young adults look to be fully grown, but they do not attain maximum size and weight until eight to ten years of age.

Cubs are sometimes deserted by the mother, who has the urge to mate, when they are yearlings under two years of age.

first shoots of tender plants appear. However, the youngsters do not suddenly switch to solid food and forsake the mother's milk. In Alaska a mother fed fish to her cub on August 21, while another cub only the day before did not eat fish. Cubs with their parent ate the meat that I was using for photographic bait, and these same little ones were still nursing. I saw two cubs suckle during the last week of August when they were more than seven months old, but I have never seen nursing cubs older than this. However, the Craigheads stated: "Not until the youngsters are weaned, some as yearlings and some as two-year-olds, will sows accept the attentions of the boars."

Apparently weaning is a long-drawn process, but it does not mean the separation of the family at its conclusion. The mother remains with her cubs during their first and second years. However, in their second autumn, when the young are a little less than two years old, she may

Beaver are sociable animals.

Canada geese, which are gregarious, migrate in large flocks.

desert them and seek a solitary winter den. Or she may keep the family intact until the mating season of the following summer. At this time the offspring are about two and a half years old and, though not sexually mature, are self-reliant and no longer dependent upon their parent. When this separation occurs it is final; once the family breaks up the young do not reunite with their mother.

Some animals, such as ants and beavers for example, are said to be social because they live more or less in organized communities. Others habitually live or move about in flocks or herds: the Canada goose congregates in flocks during migration seasons, and the buffalo habitually lives in herds. The grizzly bear, however, is not a social animal and it is not gregarious. All of those that I have seen were either solitary animals, family groups, mated pairs, or subadults that were probably brothers and sisters. In agreement with this, Enos A. Mills stated: "The grizzly leads a solitary life. Alone he hunts for food, alone he wanders for adventure. Singly he fights his foes, and in solitude he dens up in winter. A possible explanation of this may lie in the fact that being alone is an advantage to an animal of his size and enormous requirements."

However, under certain conditions a number of bears may congregate in the same area. In 1840, a drove of sixteen California grizzlies was seen feeding on acorns. On another occasion nine bears were in the same berry patch. More recently, in 1963, thirty grizzlies regularly fished at the same time at the McNeil River falls in Alaska. It is evident that these bears were grouped only for the purpose of eating. The abundance of food at any place gives practically all grizzlies public rights. A berry patch or a salmon stream may become a community feeding place, and a number of big bears may eat peacefully within a few yards of each other.

It has been my experience that tolerance of animals toward others at feeding places is not limited to the grizzly bear. Birds at my feeders eat together, and during the winter I often see blue jays, starlings, and

Buffalo are also gregarious and live together in large herds.

sparrows almost touching each other as they eat seeds, corn, and bread. At other seasons, when no snow is present, the jays chase the starlings and the starlings, in turn, chase the sparrows. In this order of dominance the largest birds eat first; the smallest eat last.

The aloofness and the indifferent attitude of grizzlies toward each other is very interesting. Congregated at a good salmon riffle or a large berry patch, they fish or eat side by side but they completely ignore each other. This is rather like humans who eat alone in a restaurant and ignore the people at nearby tables. However, subadults and young sexually mature grizzlies avoid large bears by sneaking off or by remaining at a safe distance. Smaller bears ran away from my photographic bait when a big grizzly came to eat, and the smaller bears did not return until the big one had left. The Craigheads summarized this by stating: "Dominance based on size, aggressiveness, and experience is the key to stratification of grizzly society."

Dominance between bears may even be expressed in bathing. At a distance of perhaps eighty yards I was watching a black bear splashing about in a shallow forest pool. Through my binocular I saw the black bear suddenly sneak off, and in a few minutes a big grizzly waded into the water and sat down. It dangled its front feet below the surface and moved them about. Then the bear lay back and rolled so that at times its head was under water. Finally it waded ashore, shook the water from its coat, and left. The bath took less than five minutes.

Autumn

EVERY ANIMAL has a home range or a territory to which it restricts its activities. The grizzly is no exception. It has a home range, the size and location of which depends basically upon the available food supply. The extent of any creature's territory is generally governed by its size: a field mouse may live and die on a plot of grassland 100 by 100 feet, but the grizzly demands a much larger area.

Enos A. Mills confirmed this fact and added:

A grizzly has his own home territory. In it through the seasons and through the years he makes his living; he defends it against invaders, and in it he commonly dies. Although he does not tolerate other grizzlies on his home range, different kinds of animals not in competition with the big bear may use it. These species may include mountain lions, wolves, deer, moose, and others. Co-existence is possible and it is practiced.

When pursued the grizzly tries to keep within his domain. Usually he travels only 7 or 8 miles in one direction. Only two or three times when trailing bears have I known him to travel more than 14 or 15 miles in one direction.

The Craigheads have tranquilized grizzlies and attached collars with radio equipment to the necks of the animals. This has enabled them to locate and follow the activities of individual bears without even seeing them. They stated: "Radiotracking reveals that a few grizzlies use only 10 to 12 square miles of Hayden Valley. But one bear, Peg Leg, foraged

106

The grizzly's range is shared by other animals. Pronghorns (right), elk, deer, and others are not competitors of the big bear, and they coexist peaceably.

in summer over 168 square miles. . . . During a week-long ramble, Peg Leg traveled 100 miles and swam the Yellowstone twice, once after descending a precipitous wall of the Grand Canyon of the Yellowstone."

Thirteen by thirteen miles is 169 square miles. A range of 6½ miles in any direction from a center point would be equal to the range of this Yellowstone grizzly. Other bears had a home range of 4 by 14 miles, or 56 square miles, and one limited its activities to an area 3 miles by 5.

Grizzlies will occasionally move to a new range if the supply of food becomes scarce, if they are persistently persecuted by hunters, or if the territory becomes overcrowded with other bears. Another normal and annual short migration is from summer range to winter quarters.

Wild and domestic animals, as well as humans, have an attachment to their homes. Man becomes lonesome for the old neighborhood, and dogs and cats have returned unescorted to their homes from great distances. I once read an account of a collie dog that returned 135 miles

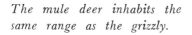

The mule deer inhabits the same range as the grizzly.

Grizzly bear habitat: food and sunshine in the open areas; shade and cover in the forests; denning sites at higher elevations.

to its home. The animal had been lost, and the owner drove home in his auto without it. The grizzly has evidenced this same fondness for its home area. A. H. Macpherson related that grizzly bears in Canadian national parks that had been transported up to 38 miles returned to their capture points before resuming their normal activities. The Craigheads released many of the Yellowstone grizzlies where they were captured. Others were taken 25 to 35 miles away and then released. Most of the bears returned to their home territories, some within two or three days.

A grizzly cub raised by Philip A. Rollins was not chained or caged. When four years old it was taken far from the Rollins ranch and turned loose. The bear was back at the ranch eight hours before the return of its keeper.

Most wild animals protect their home territories and chase trespassers if they are of the same species. I have seen woodchucks and red squirrels defend their holdings against others of their kind, and it seems that the grizzly is of the same mind; the strongest and oldest bear can claim and hold any area it desires.

The type of habitat in which the grizzly dwells is governed more or less by climate, shelter, and food. I have seen grizzlies on the open prairies, in forests, on the shores of ponds and streams, at rather low elevations, and on mountaintops near timber line.

In the western United States it seeks high, rolling meadows and open thickets. There it can find the warmth of unobscured sunshine and also shady retreats. It finds hiding places in the thickets and both plant and animal food in the open. In Alaska it favors open tundra and grasslands and mountain meadows with forests nearby. The greatest population lives where there is an abundance of lush grass, such as on Kodiak Island. This type of habitat is important for the bear's survival because it provides early spring food for the hungry animal. There are no restrictions on the wanderings of the grizzly, though, and the same bear may be in the lowlands fishing for salmon one day and on a mountaintop the next. It seems as though the huge beast goes to where its food is, and when no longer hungry it seeks rest, comfort, and a hiding place. On cold days it basks in the sunshine, and on hot days it seeks the shade.

My experience with the grizzly leads me to conclude that it is most active late in the afternoon, just before dark, and at night. Because of this, many of my photographs were made with the use of flash equipment during the darkest hours. Wright reported: "Where hunted or disturbed he will feed at night or just before break of day or at dusk. Where it is free from annoyances he will feed up to 10 A.M. and from 2 in the afternoon until dark and perhaps longer." John M. Holzworth learned, during his studies of the Alaska grizzly in 1927 to 1929, that where it

Grizzlies are most active in late afternoon, just before dark, and during the night.

was not molested, as on Admiralty Island, it fed at any time of the day.

In his 1963 studies of the big brown bear in Alaska, Albert W. Erickson concluded that large males feed predominantly at night, at dusk, and at dawn. Other bears feed intermittently throughout the day. Smaller bears and mothers with cubs are active on the salmon streams when and where the big males are not present.

As Tracy I. Sorer wrote of the past:

Under primeval conditions the grizzlies were active both day and night. The bears had nothing to fear from other animals and the time of foraging probably reflected their state of hunger. Some early observers state that the grizzly was active mainly at night but others mention seeing or encountering bears either singly or in aggregation in daylight hours. Many people met females and cubs in the daytime—the fast-growing

110

cubs had good appetites. As settlement proceeded and the bears were hunted extensively they became more wary and more nocturnal.

What of the bears that live in the far north, in the land of the midnight sun? There, during the summer, there is no night and obviously no truly nocturnal grizzlies. It hardly matters when they are active because there is no darkness to conceal them.

Those who know the bear may detect its presence without ever seeing the animal. One telltale sign is the bear trail, a path worn fairly deep in the earth. Other mammals have trails, too, and the white-tailed deer goes from place to place over more or less distinct paths known as deer trails and deer runs. In open fields where woodchucks live, a network of pathways connects their dens and leads from one field to another. Even the small meadow mouse keeps open a maze of trails that is concealed from view by grass and other vegetation.

A grizzly bear trail across "grassland."

The World of the Grizzly Bear

Bear trails are different from all others and need never be confused. Each bear following the same trail steps in exactly the same tracks of those that went before it, and the result is a series of single footprints. The deepest prints that I found measured a little over three inches, but Holzworth saw bears' trails six inches deep. Storer mentioned grizzly trails that were a succession of pits eight to ten inches deep and fourteen to sixteen inches apart. However, Victor H. Cahalane recorded the deepest tracks when he wrote:

I have seen bear paths that were so straight they might have been laid out with a surveyor's transit. Furthermore, each one steps in the footprint of the one that went before. The great circular footholes may become ten to twelve inches deep. In time the rows of holes may merge into two parallel ruts. Trails laid out by humans and then abandoned are sometimes kept open for decades by traveling bears.

Bears prefer to go from one place to another over these regular trails, and many different individuals may use the same paths. The trails are used year after year, and that is why they are often worn quite deep. The bears, however, when seeking food or for other reasons, disregard their paths and roam about at will.

I have followed bear trails through forests and across open slopes, and I noted that cartain bears coming to my bait always followed the same trail. Holzworth observed that, in Alaska, they have paths that they follow to and from their fishing spots and also to berry patches and other favorite feeding areas. In some places, it seemed to me that the trails deliberately led through concealing cover.

Both black bears and grizzly bears have the same habit of walking on trails. I once followed a path through an eastern forest, attached the bait, and placed my camera and tripod on the open pathway. During the night a black bear moved along the trail and came within three steps of me. When I spoke it went off into the forest and I suddenly realized that I was not on a man-made path but on a bear trail. That was many years ago, before I had learned about bears and their habits.

112

Aside from the bears themselves, I have never seen any other animal except the coyote walking on bear trails. There seems to be no reason, however, why wolves and other creatures should not use them, unless the deep footholes make walking difficult.

Another grizzly bear sign is its nest or bed, a hollow in the ground, dug by the bear, and used for resting and sleeping. One that I measured was 39 inches by 52 inches and about 12 inches deep. Another was 42 by 57 inches and 14 inches deep. One was in a lodgepole-pine forest; the other in a stand of aspen saplings about thirty feet from a bear trail. Each of these nests had bedding of pine needles, twigs, and leaves scraped in by the bear. Some, according to Hubbard, are about five feet across and 1 or 2 feet deep. In Alaska, Holzworth found beds 4 or 5 feet in diameter and from 1 to 1½ feet deep.

Besides bear trails, nests, dens, and tracks, there is yet another bear sign. This is the bear tree. Grizzlies and black bears both have the peculiar habit of standing on their hind legs and biting and scratching trees. Why they do this I do not know, but others have expressed opinions.

A bear tree.

A black bear marking a bear tree.

The World of the Grizzly Bear

Victor H. Cahalane noted:

. . . trees were deeply scarred by bites and scratches. Frequently the deepest gouge, where more of the bears have bitten, is about 6 feet above the ground. The deepest scratches may be about 12 feet high. It looks as if every bear tried to stretch and leave its mark higher than anyone else. Some hunters believe that these trees are sign posts showing who passed. Others think that the bears use them merely to stretch and relax their muscles.

Hubbard offered this opinion: "It is commonly and erroneously believed that a rubbing post is used by bears ranging in the territory to warn others to keep out of its domain. Rubbing posts are used by bears to scratch themselves, as well as to let other bears know of their prowess and proximity. Several grizzlies and black and brown bears may use the same post."

In the ocean a variety of fishes lives, and on land many different mammals exist. The grizzly has its neighbors, but few if any of them compete with the huge bear. In Alaska the grizzly may see a number of different animals, including black-tailed deer, giant Alaskan moose, caribou, wolves, Dall's sheep (which are white), bighorn sheep, and mountain goats, which also are white. In other places the grizzly bear may share its domain with coyotes, mountain lions, elk, antelopes, mule deer, white-tailed deer, jack rabbits, marmots, ground squirrels, and other rodents, and also the black bear.

Often, man has not learned to coexist with others of his own species and certainly not with forms of wildlife. In nature, though, many species live in peace with others of their own kind and with different species also. Bison dwell contentedly in large herds and peacefully share the same range with pronghorns and elk. The grizzly and other animals are also a part of the same environment.

It seems that animals are more tolerant than is generally supposed. I once saw a coyote resting near a bear trail. When a grizzly walked past, instead of running away, the coyote merely moved off about twelve

Jack rabbits are neighbors of the grizzly.

Elk and grizzlies share the same habitat. When a bear appears, the elk do not panic—but they look occasionally to be certain that the grizzly is at a safe distance.

feet and lay down again. On another occasion I saw a grizzly and a coyote walking toward each other on the same bear path. When they were about twenty feet apart, the coyote left the trail but continued walking toward the bear. As the animals passed they were not more than eight feet from each other. However, not all animals are so trusting. Early one evening, before dark, I was watching a bull moose feeding at the edge of a willow bog. About half a mile away a grizzly bear appeared. Although the moose could not see the bear, the bear's scent must have reached the moose, because it skulked off into the forest.

While watching a small band of elk, I saw a grizzly bear turning over stones on a hillside about a quarter of a mile from the elk. The animals continued to feed and to look toward the bear occasionally, but they did not run away. Hubbard, who had similar experiences, wrote: "I have seen grizzlies feeding close to deer, elk, mountain sheep, mountain goats, and domestic livestock, with the bear showing no tendency to molest them." To this Holzworth has added: "Large wild animals are customarily not afraid of him at a reasonable distance. The mountain goats will gather around to watch him dig for a marmot. I have seen deer feeding indifferently when, with their knowledge, a grizzly was within fifty yards of them. Apparently they felt safe from his attack."

The great bear seldom bothers other large animals, and in return it is seldom annoyed or attacked. However, there are records of conflict. Hubbard's father found a grizzly bear in the Wasatch Mountains of Utah that had been gored to death by a bull elk. The hunter followed the elk's blood-marked trail but never saw the injured animal.

Hubbard himself found a bull moose that had been killed by a grizzly bear. Tracks revealed that the bull, upon being surprised by the bear, ran down a slope and became trapped in a deep snowdrift.

Because of its bulk and strength the grizzly ignores the threats of all animals but man. Enos A. Mills described two episodes that reveal the grizzly's contempt for the mountain lion, the largest of all North American cats:

Before me, just at sunrise, a Grizzly and a Mountain Lion met. The Grizzly—the dignified master of the wilds— was shuffling along, going somewhere. He saw the Lion afar, but shuffled indifferently on. Within 50 feet, the Lion bristled, and, growling, edged unwillingly from the trail. At the point of passing, he was 30 feet from his trail-treading foe. With spitting, threatening demonstration he dashed by, while the unmoved, interested Grizzly saw everything as he shuffled on, except that he did not look back at the Lion, which turned to show teeth and to watch him disappear.

About the second episode Mills wrote:

On one occasion, when I was hidden and watching the carcass of a Deer which a Lion had killed, to see what carnivorous animal might come to the feast, a Mountain Lion walked quietly and unalertly to it and commenced to eat. After a few minutes the Lion suddenly bristled up and spat in the direction from which a Grizzly bear presently appeared. With terrible snarling and threatening, the Lion held onto the prize until the Grizzly was within a few feet. He then leaped toward the Grizzly with a snarl, struck at it, and dashed into the woods. The Grizzly without even looking round to see where the Lion had gone, began eating.

Near Murray, Idaho, a fight between a grizzly and a female mountain lion ended in tragedy. Edward Fergusen described it thus:

The Bear peacefully ambled along evidently unconscious of the Lion's presence when, as he approached the pile of rock where her kittens were hidden, the Lion suddenly appeared. She might just as well have remained hidden, and if she had, the Bear would without doubt have gone on his way in peace. But she didn't, and with one leap she landed square on the Bear's back. The surprised brute reared and tried to throw her off; he frantically clawed the air and tried to reach her; then he rolled on the ground; the Lion let go and with another spring was at his throat. They thrashed about, and finally, locked in each other's embrace, they rolled over the edge and tumbled down the hillside, over and over into the gulch below. When found, they were both dead, with almost every bone broken.

The hunter W. P. Hubbard is convinced that there is one, and only one, animal which at certain times the grizzly fears. This is the timber wolf, which may weigh more than 150 pounds. Wolf and bear hunters in Alaska declare that the grizzly retains its fear of wolves until it is seven or eight years old and nearly full grown.

In describing a wolf and bear fight in Alaska, the guide Russel Annabel wrote:

A mother grizzly and two yearling cubs, while feeding, approached a wolf den, and were set upon by the two parents and the two young wolves. The female [wolf] started the fight. She flashed down the slope, feinted at the she-bear, and went past to chop at a yearling's flank. An adult wolf of her race has fangs more than two inches long and jaws capable of cracking a caribou's leg bone, and in consequence the shearing cut she gave the yearling caused him to lose all interest in the fray. Squalling, he tried to crowd against his mother for protection. But the she-bear had troubles of her own. As the other three wolves closed in, she spun like a top, roaring hoarsely, and launched terrible paw strokes that never quite landed. The wolves were too fast for her, they came in from too many angles at once, and she was handicapped by the yearlings. She edged toward a pile of rocks. Like a bear beset by hounds, she wanted cover for her back. She didn't get it.

The bitch wolf slashed again at the wounded yearling, and this time the luckless little bear fled blindly down the hill, bawling in pain and terror. Without hesitation the other yearling followed at great speed. The she-bear batted again at the elusive wolves, and then, roaring defiantly, lumbered off after her offspring, which concluded the episode.

In contrast to this fight, Peter C. Lent, in the Endicott Mountains of Alaska, observed a large, mature grizzly and a full-grown wolf feeding on the same caribou carcass. The two animals were only a few inches apart. In Alaska, also, Lent and his companion, Odd Lono, saw a grizzly

Grizzlies respect the skunk.

and a wolf, both yearlings, about 150 yards from their tent. The animals, only about six feet from each other, were staring toward the camp.

Although not feared, there is a small fur bearer that the grizzly respects. This is the skunk. J. W. Revere stated that if a skunk approaches, a grizzly will retreat, with a reluctant growl, and Enos A. Mills narrated the following:

The grizzly saw the slow-walking Skunk coming long minutes before the black and white toddler with shiny plume arrived. The Skunk is known and deferred to by wild folk, big and little. Regardless of his trail rights, the Grizzly went on to a siding to wait. The siding which he voluntarily took was some fifty feet from the trail. Here the Grizzly finally sat down. He waited and waited for the easy-going Skunk to arrive and pass.

The approaching presence of the solemn, slow-going Skunk was too much, and the Grizzly just could not help playing clown. He threw a somersault; he rolled over. Then, like a puppy, he sat on an awkwardly held body to watch the Skunk pass. He pivoted his head to follow this unhastening fellow who was as dead to the humour as the log by the trail.

Bears, like humans, are not born with knowledge and understanding. They must learn, and often the hard way. One night I took a flash photograph of a grizzly and found, after processing the film, that the

An eastern porcupine.

animal had learned about the porcupine. Quills were stuck into its nose, upper and lower lips, and chin. Porcupine quills are barbed and tend to work in, not out, so that this could have been fatal. I do not know whether or not the bear recovered.

Others, too, have seen bears that have been riddled with quills of the porcupine. Hubbard knew of two hunters who heard the sound of crashing brush and the pain-filled, frightened bawling of a bear. They climbed upon a boulder nearby and saw a six-month-old cub stumbling blindly about as it bumped into rocks and trees. Realizing that something was amiss, they shot the cub and found that it had been totally blinded by porcupine quills.

This grizzly is stuck with porcupine quills in its nose and snout.

The grizzly bear was, and still is, a North American mammal of the western and northwestern part of the continent. The black bear dwells in nearly all parts of North America, from the Atlantic to the Pacific and from Florida to Alaska, thus its range overlaps that of the grizzly. In the early days, however, black bears were scarce in places where the grizzly ranged. It was reported that near Fort Jones, California, the black bear was occasionally taken, but south of there it was replaced by the grizzly. Again, in California at Kings River, the black bear became more abundant after the big grizzly disappeared. In Kern County, California, only the grizzly existed, but when it was exterminated the black bear spread into the area.

In 1887, C. H. Townsend wrote that after the grizzly bear began to disappear before the advance of the settlers, the other species become more numerous. He implied that the black bear was not abundant where the larger grizzly was well established.

We know that the black bear inhabited eastern North America and that the grizzly did not. In certain places, however, the situation is just the opposite. In Alaska, the only bear that lives on Admiralty, Baranof, Chichagoh, and Kruzof islands is the grizzly. On all the other islands south of Admiralty, according to Holzworth, the black bear is common.

In order to determine whether or not grizzlies are hosts to parasites, it is necessary to kill the bears. I do not kill animals, therefore I have not collected any external parasites such as fleas, ticks, or mites from the coat of the animal, or collected any of its internal parasites such as worms. I have not seen grizzlies scratching as dogs do when annoyed by fleas.

Bears in zoos have been known to become stiff and rheumatic with age, and Holzworth found a tapeworm in a wild Alaskan grizzly. Seton assured us that both the black bear and grizzly bear suffer from snow blindness. Erickson contended that about twenty species of parasites infest the grizzly but that these have little effect upon the health of the animal. External pests are very rare, although ticks, lice, and fleas

121

may occasionally be found on grizzlies. Internal parasites are more common and include roundworms, tapeworms, hookworms, stomach worms, and the salmon-poisoning fluke. The most dangerous parasite of the grizzly is the trichina, a small, slender nematode worm in the intestinal tract, and in the muscles of humans, which produces a disease known as trichinosis. The same worm is found in pigs, and it is this parasite that makes pork unsafe for human consumption unless it is thoroughly cooked so that all of the tiny worms are killed. Several cases of trichinosis have occurred in people in Alaska as a result of eating poorly cooked grizzly bear meat.

How can anyone tell by looking at a bear from afar whether or not it is suffering from pain or being annoyed by parasites? I once examined the skull of a bear that had two badly decayed teeth. From experience I know that a toothache is very painful. It is almost certain that this bear suffered, because bears have the same basic anatomical structure and nervous system as man and other mammals. Holzworth said of the bear: "In tearing off large slabs from tree trunks, it sometimes breaks part of the jaw. The teeth and the piece of the jawbone often adhere to the skin and continue to grow. Specimens of the jaws in this broken condition may be seen in the National Museum at Washington and at the Zoological Museum at the University of California."

Injuries of the jaw due to fighting have also been observed. A number of large males have sustained breaks in the lower jaw just back of the canine teeth. This fracture usually heals, but the lower canine teeth protrude thereafter.

When fighting, males often suffer bone-crushing blows and lacerations. The Craigheads claimed that some grizzlies die from combat.

In my opinion, man with his trap and rifle is responsible for the grizzly bear's greatest agonies. Records prove that bears have escaped from steel traps by sacrificing their toes. The cruelties of this device finally led to the abolition of the steel bear trap.

From a safe distance the rifleman can shoot a grizzly, but the bullet does not always result in instant death. It was learned that many of the famous wild grizzlies carried old wounds. Bloody Paws had been wounded at least three times by bullets; Red Robber had an arrowhead imbedded in his back and two bullets in his body; the Bandit carried several pieces of shattered bullet in his right shoulder and another bullet wound on his left shoulder. Soldiers know that shrapnel and bullet wounds cause pain, and many suffer for years after the wounds have healed. There is every reason to believe that pain suffered by grizzlies is just as severe. And there is no first aid on the hunting field and no helicopters to fly a wounded animal to a base hospital.

The food of the grizzly consists of what is available, and the supply is generally influenced by the season. Fresh young plants appear in the spring, berries in the summer, acorns in the fall, plus many other plants and animals at various times. Because the warm summer is the time when good food is most abundant, bears as well as other animals are usually in their best physical condition at this time. In late summer and autumn, however, hibernating and winter-denning mammals begin to gorge themselves. The woodchuck fattens and so does the bear. Sterling Eide reported that mature Alaskan male grizzlies gain as much as three or four hundred pounds at this time. Macpherson, who agreed, wrote: "Their urge to fatten themselves before denning occasionally drives the grizzly bears to depredations on cached supplies of caribou meat intended for winter use by small Eskimo groups that still inhabit the interior, on the middle Thelon and Contwoyto Lake region in Canada."

It is at this time, too, before the earth is frozen, that the grizzly devotes a great deal of time and energy in digging out marmots and ground squirrels that are already hibernating. At this time, also, it may dig its winter den.

Winter

TODAY WE KNOW that certain beliefs accepted by early writers of natural history are not true. Only forty years ago, the famed naturalist, Ernest Thompson Seton, declared that the bear, raccoon, skunk, woodchuck, chipmunk, jumping mouse, and bat were profound hibernators, and he referred to them as the seven sleepers. Since then we have learned that of these animals only the jumping mouse, woodchuck, and bat truly hibernate. The grizzly bear is not a hibernator, but it *is* a winter sleeper.

During the winter, when inactive, the bear's heartbeat is slower than normal and its breathing is reduced to four or five complete respirations a minute. This is about the same rate as a person in deep slumber. Its body temperature remains normal, and the animal is semiconscious. Its cold sleep is not always uninterrupted, for it may be fully aware of its

Unlike the grizzly bear, the woodchuck is a true hibernator. Here, it is rolled up as when sleeping.

Because they do not hibernate, grizzlies sometime appear outside their dens during winter.

surroundings at times. This is quite different from true hibernation. For comparison, let us consider the woodchuck. During its hibernation this animal is completely torpid and actually appears to be dead. It takes only one breath every six minutes, and its body temperature is reduced from the normal 96.9 degrees Fahrenheit to about 38 degrees. Unlike the deep-sleeping grizzly bear, the hibernating woodchuck is not semi-conscious and is not aware of anything.

A bear can be routed out of its winter quarters without difficulty, and a moment after it comes forth it is mentally alert and physically fit.

Rarely does a deep-sleeping hibernator like the woodchuck appear at the door of its den in midwinter, but not so with the drowsy grizzly.

Enos A. Mills wrote:

One winter day, I saw a grizzly's nose thrust out of a hole in the snowy slope. Then his head followed. Sleepily the grizzly half opened his eyes, then closed them again. His shaking and drooping head fell lower and lower, until with a jerk he raised it only to let it droop again. Evidently it was the head of a very sleepy grizzly. Occasionally he opened his eyes for a moment, but he did not seem interested in the outside world and he finally withdrew his head and disappeared into the den.

After midwinter, and especially toward spring, a bear sometimes comes out for fresh air and exercise, or to sun himself. One gray February day, I saw a grizzly walking round and round in a well-beaten pathway in the snow. Occasionally he reared up, faced about, and walked in the opposite direction. His den was nearby. Half a mile farther on I came upon a bear trail near the entrance to another den. Here the bear had walked back and forth in a pathway that was about 60 feet long.

About the middle of March, I examined much worn pathways near a grizzly's den. These had been made at least three weeks before and had been used a number of times. One led to the base of a cliff that faced the east, where the bear had probably lain in the morning sun. Another led to a much used spot that caught the afternoon sun.

Harold McCracken made similar observations and claimed that when bears first emerge from their winter sleep, they often spend a few days just walking back and forth to get the kinks out of their muscles. In so doing they make a well-beaten pathway.

The reasons that the big grizzly confines itself during winter are apparent. First, it escapes the cold and deep snows of the season. But it is shortage of food that makes it imperative for the grizzly to retire into its winter sleep. This sleep is an adaptation for survival; without available food many bears would starve to death. Mills has added a note of interest: "The rest which hibernation gives to mind and stomach, with the entire organism relaxed, may both increase efficiency and lengthen life."

All grizzlies, however, do not indulge in the long winter slumber. Seton wrote that over much of the southern part of its range, the grizzly does not make a winter den in which to escape the bad-weather time and probably never dens there at all. In contrast to this, William Wells pointed out that, in the Rockies, bears go into winter quarters usually in November when the first heavy snows and cold weather begin.

In the interior of Alaska and northern Canada, denning may begin in

In the southern part of its range, the grizzly may not enter into a long, cold, winter sleep.

late October and extend until late May. Along the Alaskan and Canadian west coast, the bear generally dens during November, although some may still be seen in early December fishing along the upper creeks. Males usually den later and come out earlier than females with cubs.

Apparently the time of retirement and duration of the grizzly's long winter sleep vary and are governed by the locality in which the animal lives, by weather conditions, and by the sex and physical condition of the bear. In some parts of its range, the grizzly spends half its life in winter dens.

How do bears know when to seek their sheltered winter lairs and begin

127

their cold winter sleep? We do not know the answer any more than we know what prompts the Canada goose to take off at a certain time and start its long migration flight. During their studies in Yellowstone National Park, the Craigheads found that all the grizzlies went off to bed at the same time but on a different calendar day each year. In 1961, the bears sought their winter dens October 21 and October 22; in 1963, they disappeared November 5; and in 1965, they entered their cavernous lairs November 11.

Frank Craighead felt quite certain that the grizzlies waited instinctively for a drifting, blowing storm that would cover their tracks when they went to their winter quarters. In so doing, the bears, whether they knew it or not, eliminated the possibility of being followed to their dens.

Bears eat very little just before retiring for the winter, and when they go to sleep the stomach and intestines are clean and empty. The stomach is drawn up into a solid lump like a chicken's gizzard. These were the words of the bear hunter, William Wells. With this Mills agreed, reporting that during the four or five days immediately preceding retirement, grizzlies do not eat a single thing. He then wrote: "I have examined a number of grizzlies that were killed while hibernating, and in every instance the stomach and intestines were empty." Holzworth also claimed that during the time of the cold sleep the grizzly's intestines are usually empty and the anal opening is closed by a resinous plug known to hunters as the seal.

In a winter den there may be any one of the following: a single full-grown adult; a mother and her cubs (these cubs may be newly born, yearlings, or two-year-olds); one, two, and possibly three subadults (well-grown young recently separated from their mother) that are brothers and sisters; one sexually mature young grizzly of either sex; or a pair of sexually mature young bears, the female of which has not yet given birth to her first offspring.

Others agree with my conclusions about the occupants of winter dens. Wright stated:

128

Winter

I cling to the belief that no two full-grown grizzlies go into the same den for winter. I have seen as many as four grizzlies come out from one den, the mother and her three cubs.

I once found six winter dens in the Selkirks in a single day and as the tracks showed, not more than one bear had come out of any of the six dens.

During the sleeping period in winter the grizzly does not eat but survives on its extra body fat. Other creatures also live for long periods without nourishment. Each year penguins make a sixty-mile trek across ice fields in the Antarctic to their nesting sites. After mating and nest building, the females return to the sea and the males alone incubate the eggs. During this entire time, and until the young are hatched, these males do not eat, and the duration of their fast may be several months.

The grizzly bear is the champion of all diggers. Its powerful shoulders, sturdy arms, and long, sharp claws are its tools. In summer and autumn it digs for rodents, and before the ground freezes and the snows come the wise bear digs its winter den. Grizzlies are big and so are their lairs. The bedroom is about 4 to 8 feet in diameter and 4 to 6 feet high. There is always a bed, composed of a thick carpet of leaves, grasses, shreds of bark, twigs, and evergreen boughs. There is no bathroom but none is needed, for the grown grizzly does not excrete during its winter sleep.

Grizzly bear den.

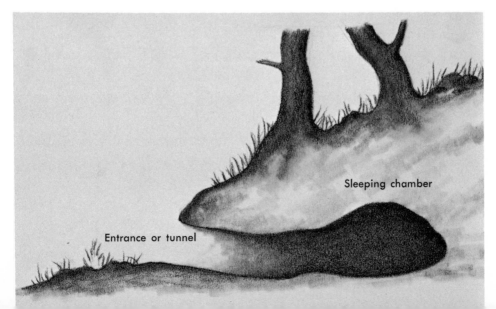

James Mackenzie, who saw a number of grizzly dens, asserted that he never found dung in any of them.

A tunnel about 3 feet wide and 4 feet high leads from the entrance to the sleeping quarters. The length of this may vary from 6 to 12 feet. In digging its winter den the bear may remove 200 to 300 cubic feet of earth. A hole 8 feet long, 6 feet wide, and 6 feet deep contains 288 cubic feet of soil, and the grizzly in digging its den may remove this amount of earth and sometimes more.

One den that I examined was on a gentle slope in a pine forest. The tunnel leading to the sleeping chamber was nearly straight and near the center was a little lower than at the entrance. The highest part of this tunnel was 4 feet 3 inches and the greatest width was 3 feet 2 inches. From the entrance to the bedroom was 8 feet 9 inches; this cave was 6 feet 4 inches long and 5 feet 2 inches wide. The highest part of the den was near the center and was 5 feet 1 inch high. There was a bed of leaves, twigs, and small branches of evergreen. In it I found some hairs, the shortest of which was $2\frac{1}{8}$ inches; the longest $3^{11}/_{16}$ inches. Probably the short hairs were from the bear's belly and the long ones from it's back.

There was a pile of earth at the entrance, but it was not so pronounced as the mound at the doorway of a woodchuck's burrow. It seems as though the bear scatters the soil more than the woodchuck does. The earth removed by the bear covered about a 6-foot area on either side and 8 feet directly in front of the burrow. The mound was rather fan-shaped with the greatest depth near the entrance to the tunnel. Here it was 2 or perhaps $2\frac{1}{2}$ feet deep, but an accurate measurement was not possible because this was not a new den and some plantlife had already begun to grow on the mound. At the very edge, the soil was spread out thinly because there it was farthest from the digger.

The grizzly merely scoops the earth out in order to make a cavernous den, and the mound at the entrance is not functional. The platform of earth at the entrance to the woodchuck's den, however, is very useful. There the animal may sprawl in the warm rays of the sun, ready to

The mound in front of the woodchuck's den serves as a lookout platform.

tumble into its burrow to safety if need be. And there it may also sit erect and watch for possible foes.

Jack W. Lentfer measured a den dug by an Alaskan grizzly. The tunnel and chamber were 9 feet 8 inches long; the tunnel was 2 feet 6 inches wide; the chamber about 5 feet in diameter and an estimated 4 to 5 feet high. A mound of dirt about 5 by 7 feet and 2½ feet high was in front of the den.

A den in Montana was dug where several roots grew close together. The bear had chewed one of these off in order to make an entrance and had then dug the den between a boulder and the roots. The Craigheads, in telling of four grizzlies' dens in Yellowstone National Park, wrote:

All had dug dens. None used natural shelters. All these dens were lined with evergreen boughs for warmth. They had been dug into slopes, minimizing accumulation of water during winter thaws, and all faced north, assuring a deep, insulating snow blanket.

The grizzlies had hollowed their dens at the bases of large trees, with the entrance located between thick, steeply descending roots.

131

The World of the Grizzly Bear

In view of the findings of the Craigheads and others, it seems that the denning habits of the black bear and the grizzly bear differ in at least one way. The grizzly does not use natural shelters and actually digs its own den. The black bear, so far as I have observed, seeks natural caves, hollow logs, and brush piles. It seldom digs its own den.

W. P. Hubbard also observed that grizzly dens are most often located on northern slopes, in the shaded recesses of narrow canyons, or in deep ravines. Such locations receive less sun, and consequently the bears are out of hibernation before melting snow water soaks the den. He also noted that grizzlies like to den in high country, near or above the timber line.

Mills located dens at 11,000 feet, and he too mentioned that they were upon the cooler northern and eastern slopes. In Alaska many bears den above timber line, and in Colorado a number of lairs were at about 12,000 feet.

The black bear is also a winter sleeper but not a hibernator, becoming very fat each autumn. But it seldom digs its own den.

Winter

After studies in Yellowstone National Park, the Craigheads concluded that the Park grizzlies move from summer ranges to higher elevations between 8,000 and 9,000 feet to den. Most dens are dug well in advance of hibernation. A bear may winter in the same location year after year and even in the same den.

In Alaska, a number of dens were at much lower elevations than those found by Craigheads in Yellowstone National Park. Lentfer located grizzly bear caves at 1,000, 1,100, 1,150, 1,200 and 1,600 feet.

When the grizzly retires to its winter den, fat has accumulated in its body cavity and in a thick layer just under its skin. Dr. Saxton Pope stated that at the end of autumn this adipose layer may be nearly six inches thick. So at this time the bear is fattest and heaviest. This is also true of most hibernating animals. For example, the woodchuck is very fat in the fall of the year and may be more than 25 per cent heavier than it was the previous April. Fat is an insulation, a heat producer, and a source of energy to the sleeping animal. The winter coat of the bear is additional insulation for it. Each year the old coat is gradually molted and replaced with a new one. The woolly undercoat is very dense, and the guard hairs are three inches or more long.

During summer and autumn the grizzly has turned over hundreds of rocks; it has dug deep in the earth for ground squirrels and marmots; it has excavated a big, roomy den. This work has worn its claws until they are relatively short and blunt at the time it goes into winter seclusion.

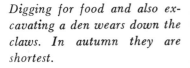
Digging for food and also excavating a den wears down the claws. In autumn they are shortest.

These bears lost weight after they emerged from their winter sleep.

During its sleep, the claws continue to grow, and when the big bear emerges from its winter lair in the spring the claws are long and somewhat pointed. Its furry coat is still long and thick, although some of it may have been shed, and the bear is just about as fat as when it retreated into its subterranean home.

Generally the homeland of the grizzly is snowbound and desolate when the animal first emerges. Food is very scarce, or there may be none at all, and it is now that its starvation diet causes the grizzly to lose weight. The store of fat is drawn upon; fortunately this supply is adequate because it practically sustains the animal. Gradually plants begin to grow, and food becomes more and more abundant with spring and summer.

There seems to be a long list of fallacies about the grizzly bear. One is that no pregnant female grizzly has ever been killed by hunters. This can be explained. After fertilization in midsummer, the ova are small, free-

134

floating, and recognizable as impregnated only by experts. While rapid growth of the embryos is proceeding, the female is in her winter den, and when she reappears in spring her cubs have been born. Hunting takes place in the fall when the embryos are not recognizable and again in spring when the cubs are with their mothers.

The bear hug is another fallacy that has been talked about for many years. It is a common notion that a bear will embrace a person or an antagonist and hug it to death. However, the bear is not a hugger, and the bear hug is no more than the name of a wrestling hold employed by man.

You have probably heard of the elephants' graveyard, which has never been found, and you may have heard that no grizzly which died a natural death has ever been seen. Grizzlies dead of natural causes have been found, however. Russel Annabel, an Alaskan guide, found two of the big bears that had died in their dens. Enos A. Mills came upon a grizzly bear that had perished in a forest fire; another died in a flash desert flood, one was killed at the foot of a cliff by a falling stone, and a fourth was crushed in a snowslide. A number of grizzlies found in Death Gulch in Yellowstone National Park have been described; their deaths were caused by toxic gas.

Another false belief is that the grizzly is a surgeon: when wounded, it will gather leaves and force them tightly into the wound, or that it will try to heal it by applying mud.

One of the most widespread fallacies is that while in its winter den the bear sucks it paw and also its anus and in so doing sustains itself. If this ridiculous notion was true, where would the nourishment come from? The animal would, in a sense, be consuming itself.

Finally, it is generally believed that the grizzly bear rears up on its hind legs and rushes toward the foe. Drawings and paintings have illustrated this method of attack, but is has never been shown in a photograph because it is not so. When a bear charges, it gallops determinedly foward in all four feet.

135

Past to Present

IN EARLY GEOLOGIC TIMES the great cave bear, *ursus spelaeus,* lived in central Europe, as did the cave tiger and the mammoth. Its remains were numerous in caverns, and evidence establishes the fact that it persisted long after man began to roam the forests. So this bear was no stranger to the cave man. Judging by its bones, it was so like a grizzly that some naturalists have asserted the grizzly is its direct American descendant.

Remains of other bears have also been discovered in European caves, and it is known that the distribution of bears was in the past far more extensive than it is now. The "Caledonian bear," for example, so popular in the Roman arena, was imported from the British Isles.

Since that time a number of different bears have been described, and today the list includes the polar bear, the grizzly bear, the American and Asian black bear, the spectacled bear of South America, the sloth bear or honey bear of India and Ceylon, the particolored bear of Tibet, the sun bear of Malaysia, and the Syrian bear of western Asia and Palestine, which is the one often mentioned in the Bible. It is now extinct, or nearly so.

Bears are widespread and live in Asia, Europe, North America, and the Arctic islands. The one species to be found outside the northern parts of the world is the spectacled bear, which lives in the Andes Mountains of South America.

Recent analysis indicates that in prehistoric times the grizzly bear ar-

136

rived in North America from Asia by crossing the land bridge of the Bering Sea in the last glacial stage of the Ice Age. Man also invaded North America by the same route and at the same period. Both bear and man were able to adapt to the Western Hemisphere and not only to survive but to coexist.

In the early 1600's, the settlers who made their homes in West Virginia, New Netherlands, and Plymouth must have seen many black bears but never a grizzly, because the grizzly bear lived only in the West. Probably the first European to see the grizzly was the Spaniard Cabeza de Vaca and his companions. Between 1527 and 1536, this party made an overland journey that took them through our present state of Texas.

Later, 1540-42, Coronado and his band journeyed through what is now New Mexico, Colorado, Kansas, and Nebraska. He records having seen many animals including bears, tigers (jaguars), lions (mountain lions), and porcupines.

In 1691, according to the records of the Hudson's Bay Company, Henry Kelsey for the first time in history placed on record a description of the grizzly bear in northwestern Canada. More than a hundred years later, in 1805, Lewis and Clark collected a grizzly in Montana, and this animal provided the data on which the scientific description of this species is based.

In those early days the range of the grizzly was very extensive. It lived in western North America from Alaska south to the vicinity of Mexico City. It roamed the Rocky Mountains, the Sierra Nevadas, and the Cascade range. It frequented the shore of the Pacific Ocean and also the coast line of the Arctic Ocean. Its home in the southern part of its domain began at the Tropic of Cancer and extended north beyond the Arctic Circle.

It was native to four countries—Mexico, the United States, Canada, and Russia, which at one time included what is now Alaska.

More specifically, the grizzly lived in Alaska, the Yukon, Mackenzie, the western half of Keewatin, British Columbia, Alberta, Saskatchewan,

The black area denotes the range of the grizzly bear in the early 1800's.

and southwestern Manitoba. South of Canada it wandered about on the plains, climbed the snow-capped mountains, and swam in the Pacific Ocean. It lived in Washington, Oregon, California, Idaho, Nevada, Utah, Arizona, Montana, Wyoming, Colorado, New Mexico, Texas, North Dakota, South Dakota, western Nebraska, northwestern Kansas, and along a thin strip of western Minnesota. This area included seventeen of our forty-eight continental states.

Today the great grizzly bear is extinct in all the eastern portion of its former range. In the United States, south of the Canadian boundary, it no longer exists except in a few isolated areas and in several of our national parks.

We are greatly indebted to those who preceded us and left records of the past. Because of them we now know that the grizzly was at one time abundant. However, abundance is relative. Flesh-eating animals are always less plentiful that the plant-eating animals.

Although the grizzly bear was numerous when the white man first invaded its domain, it was never as plentiful as were some of the other

138

The present (1967) known range of the grizzly bear. This does not include areas where the grizzly is only believed to exist. In contiguous United States the giant bear positively occurs in Idaho, Montana, and Wyoming, while the existence of the grizzly in Colorado and Washington is doubtful.

animals. The buffalo, or bison as we call it today, was described by early explorers as being countless. Seton concluded that the maximum of these huge shaggy beasts was 75 million and that the number of pronghorns may have equaled or even exceeded this estimate. Available records enable us to conclude that the grizzly never approached the bison or the pronghorn in numbers.

The buffalo population may have been 75 million in the early days.

The World of the Grizzly Bear

In 1830, the grizzly population in California was believed to be about 10,000 animals. In Napa Valley in 1831, the hunter George C. Yount said that grizzlies were everywhere, on the plains, in the valleys, and on the mountains. He often killed five or six in one day, and it was not unusual to see fifty or sixty in twenty-four hours. He probably traveled no more than eighteen miles during daylight hours when hunting. Based upon this possibility, there was at least one bear for every three lineal miles. In the Sacramento valley in 1841, he saw sixteen grizzlies in one drove.

There were other bear hunters in California also. George Nidever killed about 200 grizzlies in Obispo County prior to 1840. In the central coast region of the state, Colin Preston killed about 200 in 1840 and in Tejon Pass in 1854, three hunters killed 150 of these huge bears in less than one year. In 1848, a party of five professional hunters brought over 700 grizzly pelts to Sutter's Fort at Sacramento.

In Idaho William H. Wright once killed five grizzlies with five shots fired in rapid succession. George McClelland in Wyoming killed nine bears in a few minutes, without changing his position.

In the seventeen western states where the grizzly bear formerly existed, the total area, based upon the report of the Geographic Division, Bureau of Census, is about 1,472,105 square miles. One half of this area might be water and other unsuitable grizzly habitat. Therefore, the bear might actually have occupied only about 736,053 square miles of this range. If there were two grizzlies on every square mile of its occupied domain, there could have been a total of about 1.5 million grizzly bears in the United States when the white man invaded the West.

The invention of high-powered rifles marked the beginning of the era of destruction for the grizzly, the bison, and many other mammals and birds. The Indian with his flint-tipped arrows and short-range bow was not a threat. Neither was the early pioneer with his muzzle-loading, single-shot, smooth-bore gun, which had very little shocking power and an extremely short range.

140

Even the famous Kentucky rifle was not a grizzly stopper, and its best range was 60 to 100 yards. It required thirty seconds for a skilled rifleman to reload this muzzle-loading flintlock, and during that time a grizzly could charge more than 300 yards.

About 1848, the large-caliber, breech-loading Sharps rifle came into use, and this weapon had grizzly-killing power. However, coupled with the high power of new guns, the most important contributing factor in the destruction of the grizzly bear in the United States was the introduction of domestic cattle, sheep, and other farm stock into the grassy areas on the grizzly's range. According to the United States Report on the Statistics of Agriculture, in Texas alone there were 100,000 head of cattle in 1830. Thirty years later, in 1860, this number had increased to more than 3.5 million.

The grizzly became the first and foremost predatory animal to the cattlemen. Cash bounties were offered for the killing of any grizzly by cattlemen's and sheep growers' associations and by local and state governments. The use of poison, and of steel bear traps were introduced, and the bear became the paramount trophy of many sportsmen. All of these factors, aided by modern firearms and trained dogs, spelled the doom of the grizzly. This policy of destruction was adopted, officially and otherwise, throughout the entire range of the grizzly in the United States. Not even the rattlesnake has had such a determined and widespread campaign of elimination waged against it.

Grizzlies were rarely hunted for their meat by market hunters until the time of the California gold rush in 1848. At the mining camp of El Dorado in 1849, grizzly meat sold for $1.25 a pound. In Sacramento in 1850, it sold for $1.00 per pound. In San Francisco in 1850, venison sold for 20 cents a pound while bear meat was 50 cents a pound. Grizzly bear steak became a choice dish at some restaurants.

Regardless of the use of bear meat during the gold rush period, William Wells assures us, bears were not extensively hunted even in the early 1880's:

141

In 1959, the grizzly bear population had dropped to 856 in the United States south of Canada.

. . . but about '89, the skins took a jump in price, and at the same time some of the Western States put a bounty on Bruin. This made hunting them profitable, and they commenced to decrease rapidly. Before this time, hardly anyone killed them except during the short season in spring and fall when the fur was good. But now, when every bear, cubs and all, were worth $10 a piece, the poor brutes had no rest.

Where now are the hundreds of thousands of grizzly bears that were part of our great American heritage? They are gone—gone forever—from nearly all of their former range in North America south of the

142

Canadian boundary. The last known grizzly in Northern California was killed in 1902, and none has lived in other parts of the state since 1922. The last two records for Oregon were in 1894, and no grizzly has been known in Texas since 1890.

The United States Fish and Wildlife Service census of 1952 gives the total grizzly population as 1,208 individual bears. In 1959, only seven years later, this number had dropped to 856, representing a decrease of one fourth of the entire grizzly bear population in the United States south of Canada. These figures include all bears in national parks, monuments, Indian reservations, and national and state forests as well as on federal, state, and private lands.

The range of the grizzly bear in the United States has been so reduced by man's occupation of its former habitat, and by hunting, that it is now limited to five western states. In two of these it is at all times protected by law; in the other three states, hunting the grizzly is permitted.

Colorado. In this state there is no open season on the grizzly bear because there it is practically nonexistent. In a Colorado state publication, Howard Stiehm wrote: "Now, if there are any grizzlies at all in Colorado there are not more than a dozen or so in remote parts of the San Juan Mountains where a management area has been set up by the Game, Fish, and Parks Department, and they are protected by law."

Idaho. The grizzly has had complete protection in this state since 1947. In 1967, it was estimated that about fifty big bears still exist in Idaho. These live in the Cabinet Gorge range north of Sandpoint, the Bitterroot Mountains of the upper Clearwater River, and near the Henrys Fork of the Snake River adjoining Yellowstone National Park. This information was sent to me by E. Kliess Brown of the Idaho Fish and Game Department.

Montana. Vernon Craig, Department of Fish and Game of Montana, informed me that there were no reliable estimates in 1967 of the number of grizzlies in the state. The yearly hunter take is thirty to forty bears and this faily constant figure indicates that the grizzly population is stable.

Montana has more grizzlies than any other state south of Canada. This is probably because of Yellowstone National Park, a 3,472-square-mile sanctuary that borders on Montana's southern boundary, and Glacier National Park in the northwestern corner of the state where, within 1,583 square miles, the bear is completely protected. All grizzlies do not remain within park boundaries, and those that wander out of these parks are, in part at least, responsible for Montana's great silver-tip population.

Washington. E. Reade Brown, Department of Game of the State of Washington, wrote me that the present status of the grizzly is very low and that possibly ten bears comprise the total population. Hunting is permitted, and in the fall of 1966 a grizzly was killed at Skagit. This was the only big bear killed in several years. The department plans to close the hunting season on grizzlies.

Wyoming. In this state, Yellowstone National Park provides an ideal habitat and also complete protection for the grizzly within its boundaries. It has the *greatest concentration* of bears in the United States south of Canada. Based upon the estimated population of 250 bears, there is one grizzly on every fourteen square miles of territory. Outside of the park, though, it is different. Rex M. Corsi of the Wyoming Game and Fish Commission wrote: "I doubt that we have over fifty resident grizzlies outside of Yellowstone Park."

Hunting is permitted from April 1 through June 30 and again in autumn. There are no annual records of bears killed by hunters, but Corsi informed me that the average take is six to ten grizzlies each year. These animals are taken near the border of Yellowstone, and they are probably park-bred bears.

Thus, from seventeen states, by 1959 the great bear had been exterminated from all except the five states of Colorado, Idaho, Montana, Washington, and Wyoming. It is possible that today the Colorado grizzly is gone and that only four states can boast of its presence.

The pyramids in Egypt were begun in 3000 B.C., and bears and Indians lived in North America long before that time. Yet it required only one hundred years for the white man almost to exterminate the grizzly, which had endured for possibly millions of years. Fortunately, men of vision have set aside beautiful wilderness areas as national parks, where the grizzly and other forms of wildlife find sanctuary. It is probable that in the near future these parks will be the only places where the wild grizzly can be seen.

Alaska. Alaska is the last stronghold of the grizzly bear in North America, and there, too, its protection is a necessity. In a thirty-year period, 1898 to 1927, Allen E. Hasselborg killed more than 300 Alaskan grizzlies. In 1922, Howard McCracken saw a total of 197 grizzlies in one year on the Alaska Peninsula. John M. Holzworth observed 18 bears on the day of August 23, 1929. In that same year he saw 105 big bears during a thirty-four-day period and photographed 75 of these. In the opinion of Kim W. Clark, the big brown bears on the Kodiak Islands numbered about 2,000 in 1958. The annual kill by hunters at that time was about 200.

Now that Alaska is a state it has been made more readily accessible; it seems certain that an increase in the numbers of hunters will reduce the grizzly population. Also there are plans to alter the land use of this great state, and this will shrink the area suitable for grizzlies and for other forms of wildlife, too. Finally, as the population of the state increases, the population of the grizzly will decrease. This pattern has been followed over all of the grizzly bear's range.

According to Jack W. Lentfer of the Alaska Department of Fish and Game, there is no total population estimate that would have much meaning, because grizzlies are sparsely distributed over an extremely large area of more than half a million square miles. However, hunters killed 856 grizzlies in Alaska in 1966. The average kill by hunters over the four-year period 1961-64 was 554 big bears.

Cubs and females with cubs are protected at all times. The open season for the grizzly varies in different parts of the state. Some areas have a spring and fall hunting season, while other areas have a fall season only.

Under the supervision of the United States Fish and Wildlife Service, the big bears are protected in the following places:

Aleutian Islands National Wildlife Refuge, Alaska: 3,214 square miles.

Kenai National Moose Range, Alaska: 3,214 square miles.

Mount McKinley National Park, Alaska: 3,030 square miles.

Other Alaskan wildlife refuges include Forrester Island, Hazy Island, Tuxedni Refuge, Kodiak National Wildlife Refuge, Semidi National Wildlife Refuge, Izembeck Wildlife Management Area, the Pribilof Islands, and a number of others, but not all these areas have the grizzly bear.

These and other sanctuaries are extremely important for the preservation of plants and animals alike. The population of nearly every species of fish, bird, and mammal is being reduced by man. This is due to hunting, trapping, fishing, and poisoning, which includes insecticides, along with water pollution, the destruction of natural habitat, and the introduction of domestic stock onto grassland and other wild animal ranges.

Northwest Territories, Canada. P. A. Kwaterowsky, Superintendent of Game, explained in a letter to me of May 25, 1967, that there is no estimate of the grizzy population and no record of the number of bears taken each year. This is understandable because the Northwest Territories comprise an area of more than 1.25 million square miles.

In this vast region the grizzly may be legally hunted, at times, in certain areas. In other places it is protected at all times; however, Indians, Eskimos, and Metis have inherited the right to take grizzlies at any time and in any amount that is deemed necessary for their livelihood.

Yukon Territory, Canada. The Canadian Wildlife Service, according to Dr. A. M. Pearson, has no estimate of the grizzly population in the Yukon. Hunters killed 57 of these animals in 1966, and the average take over the seven-year period 1960-67 was 62 bears. The spring hunting season is April 15 through June 15, and the later season is August 1 through November 30.

Alberta, Canada. Dr. S. B. Smith, Director of Fish and Wildlife, informed me in his letter of June 23, 1967, that there are no data on the number of grizzlies in Alberta. The animal may be hunted in the spring and in the fall of the year. There are no records of the annual kill by hunters, and Dr. Smith wrote: "Last year [1966] we would guess that there were less than 25 grizzly bears killed in this Province. In 1968 we plan to severely restrict grizzly bear hunting both for residents and non-resident hunters in Alberta, by developing a permit system which will allow only a set number of bears to be taken throughout the Province."

British Columbia, Canada. There is no official grizzly bear census and no records of the annual take of this game species by hunters. This is understandable because the area of British Columbia is 366,255 square miles. G. Ferguson, Department of Recreation and Conservation, wrote the following in a letter dated June 15, 1967: "We do have an open season on grizzly bears in British Columbia each year. It is estimated that there are 10,000 grizzly bears in this province and between 400 and 500 were taken last year."

In all of its present range there is no reliable information on the actual number of grizzlies based upon field studies and surveys except in Yellowstone National Park. There for seven years Frank and John Craighead conducted scientific studies and obtained valuable data on the grizzly population in the park.

I have written to officials in all areas where the big bear still exists, and in reply these persons provided only guesses and estimates. The reason for this is that the grizzly is distributed over a vast area of possibly 3 million square miles. Much of its range is rugged and remote, and a huge army of searchers would be required to make even a reasonably accurate count of the numbers of existing grizzlies.

Attempts at a population estimate have been made, however. In southeastern Alaska one based upon tracks was conducted. This method failed because tracks of the same animal might be counted time and again while the tracks of others might never be seen. The United States Forest Service took bear censuses by using airplanes. This was not satisfactory because only bears in the open could be observed, and many animals ran to cover when they heard the approach of the survey aircraft.

The Alaska Department of Fish and Game tried to determine the number of bears on Admiralty Island by aerial counts of bear trails in the snow during spring. This method is still being tested. Other methods have also been tried but none have been successful. Having been a professional zoologist, I know from experience that even the most thorough wild animal survey in a relatively small area is not 100 per cent accurate. However, estimates by qualified research workers based upon definite information, even though limited, are of some value. Mere guesses by hunters and by others are apt to be very inaccurate, and I have found that the tendency is always to overestimate. In my opinion there are fewer grizzly bears in North America than the estimates declare.

The Grizzly and Man

I WAS AFRAID of grizzly bears because I had read about their ferocity. When I met my first grizzly I was scared, really scared. The bear was on a mountainside turning over rocks in search for food, but it was working its way toward me and since the wind was in my favor—from the bear toward me—I waited. Soon it appeared and passed at about fifty yards, but this was too far away for a successful shot. Then the animal disappeared into a gulch and I stalked forward. At the edge of the ravine I searched for the creature, but it was not there. I saw movement, and there went the bear galloping away over the crest of a knoll. It seemed as though the bear was just about as scared as I was. Then I realized that in my fright and excitement I had left my camera in the brush when I started stalking. (I am a camera hunter, you know; I never carry a gun.)

That was more than twenty years and a great many bears ago. Since then I have been charged by three wild black bears (two of which were mothers with cubs), one bull moose, and a cow elk, but I have never been clawed, gored, bitten, or kicked by these or any other large wild animals. Furthermore, I believe now that I was never in any serious danger, but I hasten to add that I was somewhat frightened at times. However, fear is now a thing of the past. No longer do I have any qualms about being close to large wild animals because I feel that none of them really wants to attack and kill man, including the grizzly bear.

In my opinion the animals that charged me were bluffing and,

149

A black bear charging me. Note the cub in the upper right-hand corner.

because I did not run away, their bluff did not work. This is true of all except the cow elk that had a calf. She ran to me, reared up on her hind legs, and slashed down at me with her front hoofs. I threw my broad-brimmed Stetson in her face and this discouraged her. She did not run but merely walked away, and it seemed as though she was not afraid of me. An incident with a cow moose was quite different. This animal walked back and forth in front of me and grunted. The hair on her shoulders and back was raised, but she did not charge. Finally the cow nudged her very young calf, which I had not seen, and the two moved away, leaving me standing alone in a willow swamp.

Bear stories have a fascination all their own. Goldilocks and the Three Bears is a tale that has endured, and Teddy bears have been children's companions for many generations. Now Smokey the Bear is a forest fire prevention symbol. In the grownups' world, however, many bear stories

A moose cow contemplating attack in defense of her calf, hidden nearby. Note that the hair on her back is raised.

have tended to portray the bear as a bloodthirsty killer and the grizzly bear as the most deadly of all.

I have photographed a great many grizzlies, and not one has ever charged me or even shown any inclination to do so. One night when I was photographing grizzly bears, two came at the same time to feed at my bait. Something alarmed them and one ran directly toward me. When only about eight feet away it stopped, looked at me, and uttered a low *woof*. Then, ignoring me, it turned toward the bait. About a minute or so later, the largest grizzly I had ever seen appeared. The other two waited at a distance until the huge one had finished eating and had moved off into the darkness. Then they returned to their meal.

Certainly these grizzly bears knew of my presence. In fact I planned it so, for I had left a wool shirt, strong with my scent, near the bait so my odor would be associated with the food and thus get them accustomed to it.

151

I have never been charged by a grizzly.

In order to study and photograph bears, moose, and other wild animals, I work at close range. I never feel I am in any danger. However, I *am* afraid of a domestic bull, and I would not approach one in a pasture. A great many more men have been injured or killed by bulls than by bears.

A. H. Macpherson contended that those most familiar with the grizzly bear seem to be the least afraid of it. The photographer, Andy Russell, whose only weapon was a camera, was close to more than 200 grizzlies. Though he was sometimes charged, he was never actually attacked. The native hunters of Fort Macpherson, Canada, claim that a

152

grizzly is less belligerent and aggressive than a black bear and will not attack unless wounded.

Other wild animal photographers, naturalists, and scientists agree that the mighty grizzly does not attack man. Holzworth wrote: "I took close-ups (photographs and movies) of over 100; three fourths at a range of less than fifty yards, and one fourth at a range of less than twenty yards." Once, while taking pictures, Holzworth was watched by a large female grizzly that stood on her haunches behind a stump not five yards away. In another experience he suddenly came face to face with an Alaskan grizzly as he turned a little bend in the trail. It was a surprise to both Holzworth and the bear. He was so close that he could have reached out and almost touched the animal's nose. "The animal stopped," wrote Holzworth, "so I turned the movie camera on him and pressed the starting button. He stared at me in amazement for fully three seconds, then turned in his tracks and silently and calmly walked back from whence he came."

Tracey I. Storer claimed that there are accounts of grizzlies visiting camps at night, presumably in search of food, without molesting the man asleep. One bear sniffed at the ear of a man who pretended to be asleep and then went noiselessly away.

After considering a mass of evidence, Ernest Thompson Seton reached the following conclusion: "The grizzly, according to all the best authorities, never attacks man, except when provoked. That is, he is a harmless, peaceful giant, perfectly satisfied to let you alone if you let him alone."

However, grizzlies *have* attacked man. They have mauled him and they have killed him. Why? Because, it has been said, they were provoked, cornered, wounded or defending their young. Dr. William T. Hornaday wrote: "The grizzly temper is defensive, not aggressive; and unless the animal is cornered, or thinks he is cornered, he always flees from man." And flee he usually does, although he may bluff with a fake charge and then withdraw. The general opinion that the mother grizzly will defend her young against man has seldom been completely tested.

153

Usually the rifle ended her life before it was definitely known if she had intended to attack.

Only one account gives us full and authentic information on the behavior of mother grizzlies in defense of their young. Willard A. Troyer and his associates, while carrying on scientific investigations, trapped and released a number of cubs of the big brown bear in Alaska. Steel bear traps and leg snares were used for the purpose.

The mother bears, which remained with their cubs, were frightened away by loud noises made with rifle fire and firecrackers fired from shotguns and by the shouting of the men in the work party. Twelve mothers abandoned their trapped cubs when the men approached. Eleven females were expelled with a minimum of harassment. Only twelve mother bears displayed strong protective instincts and required a full half hour of constant harassment before leaving their young. One mother charged from about forty yards; she came running across a stream. At about twenty yards a rifle bullet was fired into the water ahead of her. This halted her charge abruptly.

Once abandoning their young, the females seldom returned while the men were present. A number, however, were observed waiting nearby. It is almost certain that these mother bears would have fought wolves, or any other natural foe, to the death. But man is the archenemy. In all of these experiences the bears were greatly outnumbered and subjected to a noisy situation that they had never before encountered. Armies have retreated when greatly outnumbered and when faced with superior arms, as were these bears.

These experiments seem to prove that the grizzly prefers not to attack man, however provoked. They also suggest that mother grizzlies may not always, or ever, actually attack man even in defense of their young.

According to Enos A. Mills, "Nearly everyone whom a grizzly has killed went out with the special intention of killing a grizzly. The majority of pople who hold the opinion that he is not ferocious are those who have studied him without attempting to kill him; while the majority who say that he is ferocious are those who have killed or attempted to kill him."

Old Mose, a Colorado grizzly, killed five men. However, the men were hunters who had cornered the bear and were attempting to kill it. W. P. Hubbard and Peggy Harris wrote: "William Parenteau, Colorado, wounded a female which charged before he had time to reload his gun. He stabbed her with his long-blade hunting knife and passed out. When he regained consciousness the grizzly was dead beside him. At a hospital in Denver, more than 150 stitches were taken on his head and face. He fully recovered in about a year."

A fatal incident was reported by the Associated Press, October 22, 1956: "A Fort Benton, Montana, elk hunter was fatally mauled by a wounded grizzly. Name Kenneth Scott."

Details of another grizzly killing were given to me by my late friend, Professor Alvin G. Whitney, by rangers, and by others. On Slough Creek in the great Beartooth Range, north of the boundary of Yellowstone National Park, lived a man and his wife. Throughout the area he was known as Frenchy Duret. Some thought that he was French-Canadian, others guessed that he was French and Indian. His ranch buildings were crude, well made, and sturdy, but the sagebrush flats that he pastured his few herds of cattle on were more suited for pronghorns than cows. Because of this his very small herd fed upon the more luscious greens within the park boundary, where the grazing of domestic animals is forbidden by law. While the animals ate, Frenchy watched from a nearby hilltop, and whenever a ranger surprised him he explained that he was just rounding up the cattle that had broken through the fence.

For transportation he used a team of oxen and a two-wheeled cart, which he drove through the woods over trails that he kept open for this purpose. The adjoining ranch was owned by Peter Parte, who disappeared rather mysteriously, and thereafter Duret owned the Parte spread.

Frenchy Duret had an intense hatred for grizzly bears. One rumor has

155

it that this hate grew after a grizzly had killed two pet fox terriers that were trailing the bear. This may or may not have been true, but besides hating grizzlies Frenchy Duret was a cruel, merciless killer of all wildlife. His huge steel traps were set for the black bear and grizzly alike, his spring poles were ever waiting for unsuspecting marten, and his deadly rifle brought destruction to many moose, elk, and deer. He hunted and trapped within the boundaries of Yellowstone Park, where all animals were to have found sanctuary, and his killing knew no season. In spring and summer, fall and winter, he stalked through the great forests of lodgepole pines and over sagebrush flats seeking—always seeking—those wild creatures which he could kill for their flesh and for their pelts.

Although his small beef herd did not dwindle, he sold "beef and sheep," which was the flesh of moose, elk, deer and bighorns that he poached within the great national sanctuary and toted over mountain trails in his oxcart. In the nearby town of Gardiner and Cooks City, men ate the red wild meat which they illegally bought from Frenchy Duret. His own larder was seldom empty, although in town the only supplies that he bought were flour, beans, and molasses. All else came from the land. Knowing this, forest rangers worked night and day through all seasons to stop Duret's unreasonable slaughter of protected wildlife. They watched to no avail, however, for whatever else he was, Frenchy Duret was an unusually crafty woodsman.

One day in early summer Duret came upon a huge grizzly held by a hind foot in one of his large steel bear traps. Because he did not have his rifle, the trapper went to his cabin, obtained the weapon, and returned, following with ease the trail made by the bear and the heavy drag. With confidence the hunter approached the beast, raised his rifle, and fired, but the bullet did not strike a vital spot. When the lead missile tore into its flesh, the 600-pound grizzly bawled in anguish, then leaped forward, drag bouncing behind it. Suddenly the bear tore loose from the trap and fell upon the man. A few short moments later the grizzly left the scene. Frenchy Duret lay very still.

156

The Grizzly and Man

Hours later, consciousness returned and the man began to crawl though the black night toward his cabin. Inch by inch, foot by foot, for fully three quarters of a mile he wormed his pain-wracked body over the ground. Then came the end; Frenchy Duret died as he was crawling under his own fence only a half mile from his home.

The next day his body was found and a searching party read the story in the back trail. Frenchy's gun, with one fired shell still in the chamber, was found where the grizzly had knocked it from his grasp. The bloody trail of the bear led downhill along Slough Creek and, so far as is known, the animal's offspring still inhabit Yellowstone Park.

Frenchy was buried near his cabin, and if you should visit the Silver-

Distant relatives of the bear that killed Frenchy Duret may still inhabit Yellowstone National Park.

tip Ranch on Slough Creek you may see his grave and read his epitaph:

Joseph Duret
Born in France   1858
Died   1922

These incidents of grizzlies injuring and killing men resulted only after the bears had been provoked. Blame was not put upon the men who were the aggressors. In each tragedy the bear was fighting in self-defense. The law of man allows a person to defend himself and his family against attack. If the assailant is killed it is held to be justifiable homicide. If a man's wife and children are protected, the man is acclaimed a hero. A grizzly, in doing the same thing, is condemned as a ferocious killer.

Other accounts of grizzlies attacking man shows that not one assault was unprovoked. In Holzworth's opinion: "Unprovoked attacks on the part of bears are very rare. Over this question bitter arguments have raged, and much has been written. I have read cases of 'unprovoked' attack as reported by different writers (there is much duplication of illustration) but when can one tell whether or not a bear is 'unprovoked'? Too frequently the report of the occurrence itself is garbled."

All other authorities I know of agree with Holzworth; the statements of some of these men have already been presented. Actually there are a great many known experiences in which the giant bear, even though annoyed, did not attack, but unexciting happenings seldom make the headlines. One of these incidents concerned Holzworth, who explained: "The bear began to charge from a distance of about 30 yards. I kept the movie camera on him. When about 18 feet from me, Hasselborg said sternly, 'Get back there, you fool, or I'll shoot.' The bear stopped, turned around and walked slowly away."

Here is another case. On Admiralty Island, Alaska, the party of Arthur Newton Pack encountered a big grizzly which barred the way to their boat. It charged but was stopped fifteen feet away by the guide, who hurled his hat at the bear.

The Grizzly and Man

My late friend, Mrs. Adah Lind Crist, who was the first schoolteacher in the Yukon, told me that once a grizzly walked behind and a little to one side of her. Mrs. Crist said that she was not at all afraid because bears in the territory never bothered anybody. This one was merely going in the same direction that she was.

In their intensive study of the grizzly bear, Frank and John Craighead and their research party worked for seven years in Yellowstone National Park. During that time they carried weapons against an unexpected charge by a startled grizzly, but not one of them ever had to shoot a bear.

Why is it that the grizzly bear does not attack man? It is the largest and strongest flesh-eating mammal on earth. In the past it feared nothing, not even man. But now the carefree giant that roamed about in the open and fed by day is gone, his place taken, according to Seton, "by Bears that feed secretly, silently, by night, in cover—always secretly. And what is it that made this change—that has turned the heart of the mountain terror and made him shyer than even Fawn or Hare? The educating force was modern guns."

To this can be added the words of Theodore Roosevelt: "Constant contact with rifle-carrying hunters, for a period extending over many generations of bear life, has taught the grizzly by bitter experience that man is his undoubted overlord, as far as fighting goes; and this knowledge has become a hereditary characteristic. No grizzly will assail now unprovoked, and one will almost rather run than fight."

It should not be construed, however, that because the grizzly is peace-loving it is cowardly. Holzworth affirmed that grizzlies are not ferocious, but they are courageous. Contact with man has not changed the bear from a savage and aggressive animal; contact with man has, however, added considerably to the grizzly's caution. Education has taught him discretion. The biggest of our flesh-eating mammals has learned to shun man, but this is an act of wisdom, not of cowardice. It is his way, his only way, of surviving.

Bear hunters, like fishermen, have been known to tell tall tales. Since

159

hair-raising stories of savage attacks by bears are fascinating, many old-time hunters have obliged by making up colorful ones. However, some tellers of grizzly tales have been truthful, and they have the scars to prove it. Hasselborg, the Alaskan guide, had one such experience. He shot a bear and saw it fall. Believing it to be dead, he turned his back on it to place his rifle against a bush and draw his hunting knife. Turning, he saw a mountain of fur directly before him. The bear's left forearm and paw were limp and drenched with blood from the wound in its shoulder. Hasselborg could not reach his rifle, so he did the next best thing. He dived into a shallow beaver ditch, face down, and lay still. The bear mauled him and severely bit his shoulder. The hunter felt his flesh being torn away; then he fainted. When he regained consciousness the bear was gone. After much pain and hardship Hasselborg reached help and was given medical attention. His courage and his conviction that one should lie still when under attack by a bear saved his life. He said: "I knew better then to move, because Charlie Littlejohn had tried to get away after being mauled by a bear that spring, and it had come back twice and bit him again; the thing to do is to lie quiet and make the animal think that you're dead." It might then be possible for a man to feign death while being mauled by a grizzly, but a great deal of fortitude is required.

From personal experience this Alaskan hunter was able to tell us that when a bear has a man down he only bites like a dog. Grizzlies do not deal any smashing and slashing blows or tear one apart with their jaws. Apparently bears bite moderately because of an innate fear of man.

An interesting report was presented by Enos A. Mills: "Three or four men who have been severely bitten and shaken by grizzlies have testified that they felt no pain at the time from these injuries. I cannot account for this. Livingstone, an African explorer, also states that he felt no pain when a lion was chewing on him."

To this I can add my own experience. I was bitten on the hand by a large Airedale dog and there was absolutely no pain. Another time I ran my finger through a planer. I felt no pain, yet the end of my finger was gone. My friend Jacob Smallenbroek had three fingers cut off while using a circular power saw. He told me that he felt no pain and did not know what had happened until he saw his fingers lying in the sawdust. All of these injuries became very painful, however, when they were healing.

Grizzly Adams had often warned Foster, his partner, that if he ever fell into the power of a grizzly his only hope of escape lay in feigning death. In this way, Adams and many others had escaped injury, for the grizzly has no interest in a dead man. Foster found an old grizzly with her cubs. He fired and wounded her. She charged and downed him; instead of lying still, he struggled and shrieked. The grizzly ripped him open and tore him to pieces.

This sounds like a terrible revenge, an instance of unrestrained ferocity. But we must remember that the man was the aggressor; the bear was maddened with wounds and made desperate by the menace to her cubs. She left the victim once he was conquered.

Intensive research has failed to uncover an authentic case of a grizzly eating human flesh or of remaining any great length of time near a human whom it had attacked.* This seems to support the widespread belief that the grizzly never molests a sleeping man. The bear hunter David Brown once said: "Why they never tackle a fellow when he is lying asleep, I never could understand. They could gobble us up mighty handy, but I suppose it's nature to respect a sleeping man."

In one known experience, a sleeping man was not safe. Jack Walsh, a teamster, was killed in 1916 at Turbid Lake in Yellowstone Park. Walsh was sleeping under his wagon. During the night, a grizzly attacked and mauled him so that he died a few day later. The park authorities explained that Walsh slept with his bacon under his pillow so that bears would not steal it. This encouraged the approach of the bear, and the man provoked the grizzly by striking it. Apparently the wounds alone

*Editor's Note: It is likely that the grizzly bear has never recognized man as its natural prey, which could explain why it does not usually attack a man, unless provoked.

161

were not enough to kill Walsh: he died of blood poisoning and peritonitis.

After the manuscript for this book was completed I was shocked by a television report that two girls had been killed by bears in Glacier National Park. These tragedies happened on August 13, 1967, and newspapers throughout the country gave the story front-page headlines. Francis H. Elmore, Chief Park Naturalist, whom I have known for many years, sent me some material, including the Glacier Park paper, *Hungry Horse News*. This newspaper presented four pages of details in a single edition. Park superintendent Keith Neilson said that these were the first persons reported killed by bears since the park opened in 1910.

Michele Koons, a nineteen-year-old college sophomore, met her death near Trout Lake. She was one of a party of five young students, working at the park, who were on an overnight hike. These young people, while cooking hot dogs, saw a bear approaching and ran to the shore of the lake. Squirt, a puppy, was with them, although it is a violation to have a dog on a trail in Glacier National Park.

The bear left in about a half hour, and the students returned to their camp to find that the animal had eaten all the food except some cookies and some Cheesettes. They collected a supply of wood, so they could keep the fire going, and about eleven o'clock got into their sleeping bags and covered their heads with blankets.

Denise Huckle said she was awakened by a bear at about 2 A.M. The creature stood above her and she could actually feel its breath. The pup, Squirt, was also in the sleeping bag, cuddled in the girl's arm. Miss Huckle said the bear remained in the camp most of the night.

At about 4:30 A.M., the beast went to Paul Dunn, age sixteen, and sniffed at the frightened boy. Then the animal bit into the sleeping bag. Dunn threw back his blanket and hit the animal. The bear was startled and backed away. Dunn ran to a nearby tree and climbed it.

Ronald Noseck, twenty-one, said, "I yelled to Denise that we had to get out of there."

162

"No, I can't," she replied. "I've got to undo the collar around Squirt's neck." Then Denise and Ronald jumped out of their sleeping bags and ran fifty yards down the beach.

"Ron shoved me up a tree," said Denise, "and tried to throw the dog up. I finally caught him."

Paul Dunn, still in the tree, related: "All of a sudden Michele yelled, 'He's ripping my arm.' By that time Ray Noseck had run down the beach but Michele couldn't get out of her bag. I heard something being dragged down the beach and I realized the bear had the sleeping bag.

"I said, 'Michele, get out of there,' and she said, 'I can't, he's got the zipper.' Then she screamed, 'Oh, my God, I'm dead.'"

The terrified young students stayed up in the trees until daylight at about 6 A.M. Then two of the boys raced to the park headquarters to report the attack and to get help. They returned to Trout Lake with rangers and found the dead body of Miss Koons. She had been dragged in her sleeping bag about one hundred yards from the camp.

That same night Julie Helgeson was killed by a bear at Granite Park, about twenty air miles from Trout Lake. The attack took place at about midnight.

Miss Helgeson, nineteen, and her companion Roy Ducat, age eighteen, hiked to Granite Park for a sleep-out. Both students were summer park employees. After eating their sandwiches, the couple talked until dark and then got into their sleeping bags. Both were clothed.

Ducat said that Miss Helgeson awakened him and said, "Pretend you're dead." Then, the boy explained, "A blow or something knocked me out of my sleeping bag for about five or six feet." The attacking bear then bit him in the shoulder, arm, and thighs, during which time he remained quiet, face down.

The bear then went to the girl and began biting. Ducat heard her say, "It hurts." Again the animal bit the boy on the back and on the legs and after that returned to Julie. Roy then heard the animal dragging the screaming girl away.

Ducat got up and rushed to the nearby trail cabin, where he contacted Don Gullet. In about fifteen minutes a search party started out and soon found the girl about four hundred feet from where the youths had been sleeping. She was still alive but died before she could be taken by helicopter to a hospital in Kalispell, forty air miles from the scene of the attack. Ducat, when he arrived at the hospital, was in shock and severely bitten about the shoulders, back, and legs. Doctors felt certain that he would recover. Five days later there was no infection and plans were made for the boy's release.

Trails in the areas of attack were closed while the offending grizzlies were hunted and destroyed. Three bears were killed at Granite Park and one at Trout Lake. All of these animals were females, and one was said to have weighed 260 pounds. This one might have been a young bear about two and a half year old. Park officials believe that these four grizzlies included those involved in the August thirteenth killings.

There are a number of factors that might have encouraged these attacks. All of the bears were park grizzlies that fed at garbage dumps and were accustomed to the presence of humans who never harmed them. Unlike grizzlies in wilderness areas, where they are hunted, these park bears had lost their fear of man.

It is evident that it was food at Trout Lake that lured the grizzly, and the scent of the puppy dog, Squirt, was probably an added attraction.

At first the bear at Trout Lake merely sniffed at the young people in their sleeping bags, and it was startled when Paul Dunn hit it. Even then the beast did not attack, and the youth was not pursued when he ran to a tree and climbed it.

Bears, and other animals, too, sense fear. These young people were terrified and the bear knew it.

In his article, "The People Versus the Grizzlies," in *Field and Stream,* March, 1968, Andy Russell, naturalist, guide, and wild animal photographer, seconds my opinions on these two fatal attacks. He and his son Charles investigated the Granite Park incident and learned that garbage had been placed in a ravine near the Chalet. This, it seems, was the usual practice, and grizzlies were lured to the spot so guests and staff members might see them. Sometimes, when one of the feeding animals was almost surrounded by people, it showed obvious signs of becoming angry. Russell was told that on one occasion the bear had been stoned.

He noted that the grizzlies at both Granite Park and Trout Lake were "garbage-conditioned, with no respect for humans, a change of character more often found among blacks and rarely among grizzlies. Ordinarily a grizzly bear will remain aloof even if it has become accustomed to eating garbage."

Russell then concludes that these two attacks were almost certainly made because the particular bears had been artificially conditioned by man until their behavior was abnormal:

"Normally grizzly bears are self-effacing, shy animals that usually retreat when encountered by humans. Direct and indirect prolonged association with somewhat careless people is more likely to blame for what happened last summer."

Regardless of the reasons, grizzly bears did attack and they did kill two teen-age girls and maul a young boy.

It is said that the Indian believed in talking to animals, and Tracey I. Storer related the following Indian tale:

Even the female with cubs, the most dangerous and unpredictable of bears, could be influenced by the proper words spoken in a diplomatic manner. Once when a small party of red men encountered a she-bear with young, the oldest and most respected man stepped forward and told her that they meant her no harm and that since she was a relative of theirs she should not bother them. The grizzly looked at them, understood, and went peacefully on her way.

Holzworth, who knew from experience the results of talking to grizzlies, wrote: "Until I met Hasselborg, I had never heard of a bear being talked out of completing his charge. Many a pugnacious man is stopped by a few stern words that cannot be misunderstood. It is usually

165

the tone and the manner of utterances rather than the thought conveyed that has the desired effect."

During summer and fall in 1927, 1928, and 1929, Holzworth studied and photographed, at close range, the grizzlies of Alaska. A number of times bears rushed at him, but none ever completed their charge. Sometimes Hasselborg, the guide, talked to or shouted at the bears in order to stop them. One grizzly rushed at full speed to within four yards. He was stopped by the guide, who rose to his feet, yelled at the bear, and pointed his rifle almost into the animal's face.

I believe that wild animal photographers and others who study animals have a tendency to talk to them. Once, when a bull moose charged, I said sharply, "Whoa, boy," as though speaking to a horse. The moose veered off, swept past me, and stopped about ten feet away. After that, the animal seemed to ignore me and waded out into a shallow river.

Another time I was shining deer at night, hoping to get some flash photos. Two eyes reflected back in the beam of my light, but when I walked to the place at which I saw the eyeshine there was no animal. Then I heard a scratching noise in an old apple tree and my light revealed a raccoon. Standing at arm's length from the tree I talked quietly to the animal. In about three minutes the raccoon came down out of the tree, walked deliberately over my foot, and ambled slowly away.

One night, on a bear trail, I got between my bait and a grizzly that was coming in to feed. When about thirty feet from me the animal stopped. I spoke softly and reassuringly to the bear and then walked very slowly off the trail. At about fifty feet I turned and saw the grizzly continuing on toward the meat. I was not alarmed, and I felt that the bear and I completely understood each other.

I had a similar experience with a black bear that came to a slab of bacon one rain-filled night. My poncho covered me and my camera as I sat twenty feet from the bait. The bear walked directly toward me, and when about fifteen feet away I said softly, "Easy does it, boy." The beast hardly hesitated, but it left the trail and went directly to the bacon,

Portrait of a bull moose that charged me.

which was wired to a tree at a height of five feet. However, the bear went in back of the tree, stood up on its haunches, and reached around the tree to get the bait. At this instant I took the picture. The duration of the flash was about ⅟₃₅ of a second and it did not frighten the bear. In fact the animal tugged at the bacon until it got the bait.

From my field studies and photography, I am convinced that wild animals have an intuition that enables them to know whether or not a person means to harm them. This may be part of what has been popularly called a sixth sense. I believe that, because of this psychological insight, wild animals have tolerated me while I photographed them at close quarters. Certainly a great many of them knew of my presence,

167

because it is almost impossible to be within good camera range of an animal without being detected by it.

Wright presented this opinion: "My experience has left no doubt in my mind but what there is some kind of telepathy between man and brute as well as between man and man; and that an interested but sympathetic watcher can remain unnoticed when the presence of a hostile one might breed uneasiness, if not suspicion, in the mind of the animal."

As an example of this I can cite the remarkable experiences of a group of Russian geologists prospecting for minerals in the Kamchatka Forest, Siberia. A wild Russian grizzly came near the camp, and they offered it a can of condensed milk. It liked the sweet milk and, according to the report, "hung around for more. That was two years ago and the big animal has become a mascot, lumbering along on expeditions like a pet dog." An account of this appeared in the *New York Sunday News,* April 23, 1967, and there were photographs of the huge bear wrestling with a man in the snow-laden forest. One picture showed the bear taking a small piece of food that was being held between the lips of one of the geologists. Here there was understanding and no fear between bear and man.

This same understanding is exhibited by wild black bears that beg for food along the highway in Yellowstone National Park and also by bears that feed at garbage dumps while men, women, and children look on. At garbage disposal pits in the Adirondack Mountains in New York State, black bears come to feed each evening during the summer, and hundreds of tourists congregate to see and photograph them. These black bears are truly wild, hunted intensively each autumn in one of our most densely populated states in which one out of every twelve residents hunts, traps, or fishes. And these same bears, so unconcerned about the people who watch them forage in summer, become elusive big game animals when the gunners invade their forests in autumn.

The Indian, because of fear and superstition, had a greater respect for the grizzly than did his white brother. The Pomo Indians, because of

A black bear begging.

their fear of the grizzly, did not allow a man to go hunting alone until he was twenty-five or thirty years old, and early in the Spanish period of California a sure way to earn the gratitude of the natives was to destroy a grizzly. Indians in general were reluctant to hunt or trap the big bear, and some tribes would not eat its flesh. Other Indians, though, did eat bear meat; some used the claws for ceremonial dances; medicine men wore grizzly hides, and some fashioned daggers from the leg bones of the bear. Many redmen had a strong feeling of kinship with wild animals, especially the grizzly. They felt that the bear was more closely related to them than was any other animal, because it often rose on its hind feet and stood man fashion. It has been referred to as the bear that walks like a man.

169

Besides the Indians, certain white men also admired and respected the grizzly. The American settlers who revolted against Mexican rule at Sonoma in 1846 designed and used a home-made flag picturing a grizzly bear, a star, red stripes, and the words, "California Republic." In 1911, the California state legislature formally adopted the Bear Flag as the state's emblem. In 1943, display of the Bear Flag beside or below the flag of the United States was prescribed by law for the state buildings and institutions, and the California grizzly bear was made the state animal. The football teams of the University of California at Berkeley are known as "The Golden Bears."

Some people made practical use of the grizzly after it had been killed. In the early 1800's a British firm purchased hides of cattle, elk, deer, pronghorns, and other wild animals from the Spaniards in California and Mexico. Bearskins were of little value and never had an important place in commerce. Today, however, because the grizzly is a vanishing breed, its hide is held in high esteem. Dressed and made into a rug, with head and claws, it is a prized trophy. Bear tallow and grease were also exported, and grizzlies were so numerous, large, and fat that a medium-sized merchant ship might be laden with oil from the hunt of a single season.

Bear grease was used by the settlers for medicinal purposes, and even today some people believe that bear grease is a cure for rheumatism and other aches and pains. The grease was also used for softening leather, including lariats made from braided strips of hide. Grizzly bear fat was used for cooking as well as for a hair dressing by young men. The skins were used as rugs on floors, for bedding, and for ground mats under camp beds.

During the gold rush in California, bear meat was food and bear rugs served as beds. Theodore H. Hittel claimed that the meat of a young grizzly resembles pork in taste and texture. David Brown averred that bear meat is the best in the mountains, and their grease makes the best butter. Biscuits shortened with bear grease are as nourishing as beans, and a man can walk all day on a few bear grease biscuits. Others liked bear meat, and grizzly bear steaks, considered to be a delicacy, were served in restaurants in small towns and in cities, too, including San Francisco.

In the Old West, wild animals were exploited. They had many enemies and few friends. Ignorance and illiteracy prevailed so that even the Catholic churches failed to recognize the rights of animals. Cruelty was not only condoned, it was encouraged. Animal fights were staged on holy days, on feast days, and on Sundays, at the Spanish missions as well as elsewhere. And priests and churchmen joined the throng in order to enjoy bloody spectacles of death, as did the Romans who had cheered the massacre of early Christians.

The courageous Spanish Californian, craving excitement, seized upon every opportunity for dangerous sport. In Spain, battles between bears and bulls were a form of amusement. In California, these fights reached a higher stage of development than anywhere else in the world. Grizzlies were captured for the fights by *vaqueros*. They rode in small bands which hunted down and lassoed the bear. The skill of these horsemen was superb and won high praise. When the bear was brought to bay, the *vaqueros* charged in from all sides and threw their ropes until they were successful in putting a loop around the animal's legs and neck. The trained horses kept the rope tight. Thus tied and choked, the grizzly was defenseless. Zenas Leonard wrote: "I have been told that some of the largest bears have been known to drag two horses a considerable distance in spite of all the exertions of the horses and riders to the contrary."

One type of fight was described by Tracy I. Storer:

After the animals had been brought into the arena, a hind leg of the grizzly would be attached by a leather cord, about twenty yards in length, to a forefoot of the bull; this kept the antagonists close and also discouraged the bear from climbing over the barrier. The bull roared, pawed the earth, but always seemed inclined to escape. However, the

171

lasso checked his course, and brought both of them with a sudden jerk to the ground.

Quite often the bull would race around the arena in an attempt to gore men over the barrier, and not the grizzly. The bear very rarely initiated the attack and often was reluctant to fight. If so he was jabbed with a large nail in the end of a pole, or he was roped and dragged again and again against the bull until the action was forced and the fight started. The bull would finally charge and usually the impact would throw the grizzly onto his back. Usually the bear, as the horns smashed against his ribs, would sink his teeth into the bull's nose. Sometimes the bear suddenly wrenched the bull's head to one side and snapped the spine or he might try to bite off one of the forefeet.

Jose Arnaz told of a bear that killed three bulls, one after another, and Bell mentioned a fight staged in Mexico between a grizzly and an African lion. The bear killed the lion so quickly that the spectators hardly knew how it was done. So degraded did these fights become that even tiny burros, or jackasses, were pitted against bears.

When injury or fatigue from combat caused the bull to thrust out his tongue, the bear never failed to seize this sensitive part, not letting go whatever struggles his adversary made. One witness to a bear and bull fight describes a struggle in which a bear, with its entrails dragging, ripped off the tongue, the ears, and part of the lower jaw of the bull. One fight is recorded as having lasted for two hours, although most of them were much shorter.

However, cruelties were not confined to the bear and bull arena. The gun, the steel trap, and poison added to the grizzly's misery. Countless bears have been wounded by hunters and maimed in traps. William Wells wrote that he saw five grizzlies in one afternoon and that he killed one of them, wounded another, and let the rest get away.

Practically all of the so-called grizzly outlaws had been mutilated by man. Bloody Paws, a Wyoming grizzly, when killed carried three old bullet wounds. Old Mose of Colorado had escaped from a steel trap but left two toes between the iron jaws. Three Toes had lost two toes in a trap. Red Robber was a Utah bear; when skinned, the hunters found two old bullet wounds, an arrowhead imbedded in his back, and many scars on his head, neck, chest, and sides. The Bandit, an Oregon grizzly, carried a bullet wound high on the hump of his left shoulder and several pieces of shattered bullets in his right shoulder. A grizzly killed in Idaho had a recent bullet wound high on his rump and another in the fleshy part of his back.

The first grizzly bear traps were not cruel; they were box traps made of logs, often called log traps. The inside dimensions were about 6 by 9 feet and they were necessarily very strong. At each end was a door so that the bear could see through, and these doors slid down from above when the animal went in and took the bait. Similar box traps, but for small mammals, are being manufactured today and are approved as humane.

The steel leg-gripping traps that followed were torture devices. In the early days they were made by local blacksmiths, and the jaw spread when

A double-spring trap used for trapping bear. (This is not a bear trap)

open was usually about 18 by 18 inches. Some, however, were 22 by 22 inches. Practically all these traps had sharp teeth secured to the jaws. These teeth jabbed into the skin and muscle so that the trapped animal could not pull its foot from between the closed jaws. Each trap was made with strong double springs that snapped the jaws together on the wrist or ankle when the bear stepped onto the pan or tripping device. These steel springs were often two feet long, so that a trap might be 6 feet long and weigh up to eighty pounds. Later, trap manufacturers produced a bear trap that weighed only forty pounds and had 16-inch jaws.

The struggle of a bear to escape from a steel trap was horrible. Hubbard, in describing one such incident, wrote:

Two traps were set near a dead buck and two days later when the trapper returned, the bear, one trap, and the section of the tree it was attached to were gone. In his tussle with the trap, the bear had dragged the tree section out of the blow downs and down a slope for a quarter of a mile.

Ricks the trapper found the trap with the chain and tree section still attached. The bear had torn and chewed its paw free. Pieces of his teeth were on the ground where he had broken them off in biting the trap. Ricks said that the tree section was too heavy for him to lift, so the grizzly's strength must have been tremendous. Ricks followed the trail for over a mile before he sighted the bear entering a stony ridge about three hundred yards away.

Harold McCracken asserted that, in order to escape, the bear might chew off its own toes, as other animals often do when trapped. Proof of this was given by Bloody Paws, Old Mose, Three Toes, and other grizzlies which had left parts of their feet in steel, leg-gripping bear traps. So horrible was this device that protests by humanitarians and others abolished the bear trap in most of the United States by making its use illegal.

Poison was another means of destroying grizzlies. Carcasses of sheep, cattle, deer, and elk, which men thought would attract grizzlies, were poisoned with strychinine, and by this means a number of bears were

In order to escape, a beaver severed its own foot and left it in the trap. Other animals do this also; grizzlies have left parts of their feet in steel traps.

killed each year. Many other different kinds of animals, however, were also killed, because poison is not selective. It will kill animals that are valuable to man, and even one's pet dog, just as it will kill the creatures for which it is intended.

One of the annoying activities of the grizzly is its occasional ravaging of unoccupied cabins and food caches. Generally the buildings entered contain odorous foods that tantalize the bear. Besides consuming the food, the bear may break and scatter anything that is of interest to it. The loss may be serious to a hunter or trapper and an even greater hardship to the Indian and Eskimo whose winter-cached supplies are taken by the bear.

Canoes are also sometimes destroyed by the grizzly. Some men believe that the bears hear the reverberation of their footfalls on the upturned craft buried under the snow. Their curiosity aroused, they dig down and through the canoe. For this reason canoes are habitually left right side up, even though they fill with rain and snow.

There have been reasons and excuses for killing the grizzly. The destroyers have had their way and there are those who still ask, "What good is the bear?" By this they mean of what value is the grizzly bear to man? To the hunter it is a highly prized game animal, although there are only three states south of the Canadian border where grizzly hunting is permitted—Montana, Wyoming, and Washington. However, there are hunting areas in Canada and also in Alaska, which is the big bear's last frontier. According to Lowell Sumner 17.5 million dollars are spent annually in Alaska by hunters, by fishermen, and by tourists who do not hunt or fish but who nevertheless are drawn to Alaska because of its wildlife. Actually, it costs just as much for a person to see and photograph grizzlies as it does to hunt them with a rifle.

Theodore Roosevelt, a hunter-naturalist, wrote: "The man with a gun is a specialist. He is looking for a particular thing in order to kill it. Generally the gun hampers full enjoyment of the wilderness. The hunter misses most of the beauty and glory of the trail. He learns but little of the character of the animal. Trailing the grizzly without a gun is the very acme of hunting."

William H. Wright admitted that he had as many thrills with the camera as with the rifle. Grizzly Adams was far happier with his live grizzlies than he was in killing other grizzlies. Emerson McMillin was satisfied to hunt without either gun or camera. Seton, the author-artist-naturalist, has given us much of the artistic side of the wilderness. John Muir was the supreme wilderness hunter and wanderer. He never carried a gun.

There are no legal restrictions anywhere on photographing the grizzly at any time, and for many the call of the wild means stalking animals with a camera and telephoto lens. The nature photographer does not reduce the population by a single animal, and this type of hunting is approved by all. To him, a photograph of a grizzly is as permanently rewarding as a bear rug to the sportsman.

Aside from its many values to many people, the grizzly is an important part of our American heritage. Once gone, it will be as irreplaceable as the passenger pigeon, Labrador duck, great auk, heath hen, and others. "No animal species, other than man, has ever been known to exterminate another," the Craigheads have assured us. "Do we possess the right to annihilate a fellow creature?"

Animals that have learned to adjust to the civilized world of man may exist longer than those that seek isolation. Red foxes, bobcats, white-tailed deer, and woodchucks still thrive in the state of New York, with its 15 million people, and the black bear roams about in the Catskill Mountains, only ninety miles from New York City. However, the grizzly in the West has withdrawn to secluded wilderness areas. I have never seen a grizzly bear on a paved main highway, nor one that had been struck or killed by an automobile. I think this is important to grizzly survival because highway mortality is high for most North American animals. I have seen deer, elk, foxes, raccoons, skunks, rabbits, woodchucks, squirrels, opossums, and hundreds of other animals that had been killed by automobiles on main roads, and my records include two black bears. Fortunately, high-speed superhighways do not pass through the rugged, isolated areas where the grizzly usually dwells.

Races of the
Grizzly Bear

SCIENTISTS HAVE DEVELOPED a system of classifying and naming mammals and other forms of life, based upon physical characteristics such as size, color, skull, teeth, and other features. The grizzly bear has been classified as follows:

It is in the class Mammalia because it is a mammal; and the order Carnivora because it is a flesh-eater, like the fox, wolf, and bobcat, for example.

Its family Ursidae includes only the bears, which in North America are the black bear, the grizzly bear, and the polar bear.

The grizzly and black bear are in the genus Ursus, which groups all bears that are similar. According to their taxonomic characters, polar bears are different from grizzlies and black bears, and therefore are not classified by scientists in the same genus.

The technical name is given an animal when it is scientifically described for the first time, which labels it correctly throughout the world, whereas the popular name often varies in different parts of the animal's range.

The grizzly bear was first described in 1815 and given the name *Ursus horribilis*. The first description of any animal is accepted as being typical of that species, and similar animals are thereafter compared with it. When sufficient variation occurs within a species, those that are not

A silvertip grizzly.

typical may thereafter be regarded by scientists as subspecies. Subspecies
are also called forms, or races, of the species.

Correctly determining forms or races of an animal is often very difficult even for the taxonomist, who is a specialist in the work. These
scientists often disagree among themselves. In 1923, Gerrit S. Miller,
Jr., included eighty-six species and subspecies of the brown and grizzly
bear in his *List of North American Recent Mammals*. Thirty years later

179

Robert L. Rausch reduced this list under one highly variable species known as *Ursus arctos.*

The Boone and Crockett Club, which is a custodian of big game records, accepted the opinion of Rausch. Because of this the smaller silvertip or inland grizzly was placed in record and trophy competition with the big brown bear.

Rausch, who is one of the foremost authorities on the big bears, continued his studies. He found that all grizzlies, whether silvertip or big brown, intermingle and interbreed and that sometimes it is not possible to determine if a specimen is a silvertip or a big brown bear. He observed great differences in size and color because of sex, age, and individual variations in all the big bears.

In 1963, Rausch concluded that there are two kinds of subspecies of grizzly bears in North America. They are closely related, and at times one cannot be told from the other. The first is *Ursus arctos horribilis,* usually known as the grizzly bear, silvertip, roachback, or simply grizzly. Its present range is from the western United States, north through western Canada and Alaska. The other grizzly is *Ursus arctos middendorffi,* variously called the brown grizzly bear, big brown bear, Alaskan brown bear, and Kodiak bear. It is the coastal and island form of grizzly and it lives on Kodiak and Afognac islands and on the Alaska Peninsula. It is the largest of all grizzlies and consistently weighs more than *Ursus arctos horribilis,* the silvertip or plains grizzly that was once so common over the western United States.

Bibliography

Bell, Charles N., "The Journal of Henry Kelsey." *Transactions,* Historical Society of Manitoba, no. 4, N. S., 1928.

Bell, Horace, *On the Old West Coast.* New York, William Morrow, 1930.

Bidwell, John, *Echoes of the Past.* California, 1897.

Butcher, Devereux, *Seeing America's Wildlife in Our National Refuges.* New York, Devin-Adair Co., 1955.

Cahalane, Victor H., *Mammals of North America.* New York, Macmillan Co., 1947.

————, *Meeting the Mammals.* New York, Macmillan Co., 1943.

Camp, Charles L., and Clyman Hames, "American Frontiersman." *Special Publication,* California Historical Society, no. 3, 1928.

Carter, C. F., "Duaut-Cilly's Account of California in the Years 1827-28." *Quarterly,* California Historical Society, no. 8, 1929.

Clark, W. Kim, "Land Mammals of the Kodiak Islands." *Journal of Mammalogy,* vol. 39, 1958.

————, "Seasonal Food of the Kodiak Bear." *Transactions of the North American Wildlife Conference,* vol. 22, 1957.

Colton, Walter, *Three Years in California.* California, 1848.

Craighead, Frank C., Jr., and John T., "Knocking Out the Grizzly for Their Own Good." *National Geographic,* August, 1960.

————, "Trailing Yellowstone's Grizzlies by Radio." *National Geographic,* August, 1966.

Couturier, M. A. J., *L'ours Brun, Ursus arctos L.,* France, 1954.

Dawkins, William, *British Pleistocene Mammals,* London, 1866.

————, *Cave Hunting.* London, 1874.

181

Day, Mrs. F. H., "Sketches of the Early Settlers of California: George C. Yount." *The Hesperian,* no. 2, 1859.

Dillon, Richard H., *The Legend of Grizzly Adams, California's Greatest Mountain Man.* New York, Coward-McCann, Inc., 1966.

Du Bois, Cora, "Wintu Ethnography." *University of California Publications in American Archeology and Ethnology,* vol. 36, 1935.

Eide, Sterling, "The Brown-Grizzly Bear in Alaska." *Wildlife Notebook Series,* Alaska Department of Fish and Game, no. 7, 1966.

Erickson, Albert W., "The Brown-Grizzly Bear in Alaska." *Federal Aid in Wildlife Restoration Report,* vol. 5, August, 1965.

————, "A Mixed-Age Litter of Brown Bear Cubs." *Journal of Mammalogy,* vol. 45, 1964.

Farnham, Thomas J., *Life, Adventures and Travels in California.* New York, 1849.

Fergusen, Edward, "Grizzlies and Mountain Lions." *Field and Stream Magazine,* 1914.

Gass, Patrick, *Journal of the Lewis and Clark Expedition.* Minneapolis, Minn., Ross & Haines, n.d.

————, *Journal of the Voyages and Travels of a Corps of Discovery under Command of Lewis and Clark.* Philadelphia, 1811.

George, Jean, "The Day the Bears Go to Bed." *Reader's Digest,* October, 1966.

Grinnell, Joseph, "California's Grizzly Bears." *Sierra Club Bulletin,* vol. 23, 1938.

————, *The Fur-Bearing Mammals of California, Their Natural History, Systematic Status, and Relations to Man,* vols. 1 and 2. Berkeley, California, University of California Press, 1937.

————, "Review of the Recent Mammal Fauna of California." *University of California Publications in Zoology,* vol. 40, 1933.

Hastings, L. W., *The Emigrant's Guide to Oregon and California,* Cincinnati, 1845.

Haynes, Bessie D., ed., *Grizzly Bear: Portraits from Life.* Norman, Okla., University of Oklahoma Press, 1966.

Henshaw, H. W., "Notes on the Mammals Taken and Observed in California in 1875." *Annual Report on the Geographical Surveys West of the One Hundredth Meridian,* 1876.

Bibliography

Herrick, B. F., "Grade-School Grizzly." *Quarterly,* California Historical Society, vol. 25, 1956.

Hittell, Theodore H., *The Adventures of James Capen Adams.* New York, Charles Scribner's Sons, 1911.

————, *The Resources of California.* San Francisco, 1863.

Holzworth, John M., *The Wild Grizzlies of Alaska.* New York, G. P. Putnam's Sons, 1930.

Hornaday, William T., *Minds and Manners of Wild Animals.* New York, Charles Scribner's Sons, 1922.

Hosmer, K., *History of the Expedition under Captains Lewis and Clark.* Chicago, 1834. (Reprinted from the 1814 edition.)

Hubbard, W. P., and Peggy Harris, *Notorious Grizzly Bears.* Denver, Col. (Sage) Swallow, 1960.

Ingersoll, Ernest, *The Life of Animals.* New York, Macmillan Co., 1907.

Jaggar, T. A., Jr., "Death Gulch, A Natural Bear Trap." *Popular Science Monthly,* February, 1899.

Kingsley, Homer, "Roping Grizzlies." *Everland Monthly,* N. S., 1920.

Koller, Larry, *The Treasury of Hunting.* New York, Golden Press, 1965.

Kramer, Raymond J., "Adult Brown Bears Climb Trees." *Journal of Mammalogy,* vol. 40, 1958.

Lensink, Calvin J., "Deformed Jaw in an Alaskan Brown Bear *(Ursus)*." *Journal of Mammalogy,* vol. 35, 1954.

Lent, Peter C., "Tolerance Between Grizzlies and Wolves." *Journal of Mammalogy,* vol. 45, 1964.

Lentfer, Jack W., "Report on 1966 Bear Studies." *Annual Project Segment Report, Alaska Department of Fish and Game,* vol. 8, April, 1967.

Leonard, Zenas, *Adventures of Zenas Leonard, Fur Trader,* ed. by John C. Ewers. Norman, Okla., University of Oklahoma Press, 1959.

Loeb, E. M., "Pomo Folkways." *University of California Publications in American Archeology and Ethnology,* vol. 16, 1926.

Macpherson, A. H., "The Barren-Ground Grizzly Bear and Its Survival in Northern Canada." *Canadian Audubon Magazine,* January-February, 1965.

Maynard, J. E., and F. P. Pauls, "Trichinosis in Alaska." *American Journal of Hygiene,* vol. 76, 1962.

McCracken, Harold, *The Beast That Walks Like a Man*. Garden City, N. Y., Doubleday and Co., 1955.

Merriam, C. Hart, "Review of the Grizzly and Big Brown Bears of North America (Genus Ursus)." *Biological Survey, North American Fauna,* United States Department of Agriculture, vol. 41, 1918.

Merrill, J. C., "A Silver-tip Family." *Trail and Campfire Magazine,* 1897.

Miller, Gerritt S., Jr., *List of North American Recent Mammals*. Smithsonian Institution Bulletin 128, 1924.

Mills, Enos A., *The Adventures of a Nature Guide*. New York, Doubleday, Doran and Co., 1923.

———, *The Grizzly, Our Greatest Wild Animal*. New York, Houghton Mifflin Co., 1919.

Mundy, K. R. D., and D. R. Flook, "Notes on the Mating Activity of Grizzly and Black Bears." *Journal of Mammalogy,* vol. 45, 1964.

Newberry, J. S., "Report upon the Zoology of the Route (Sacramento Valley to Columbia River)." *Reports of Explorations and Surveys for a Railroad from the Mississippi River to the Pacific Ocean,* vol. 6, part 4, no. 2, 1857.

Pack, Arthur Newton, "The Bears of Admiralty," *Nature Magazine,* January, 1937.

Palmer, Ralph S., *The Mammal Guide*. Garden City, N. Y., Doubleday and Co., 1954.

Pope, Saxton, *Hunting with the Bow and Arrow*. San Francisco, 1923.

Powers, Stephen, *Afoot and Alone*. Hartford, 1872.

———, "Tribes of California." *Contributions to North American Ethnology,* vol. 3, 1877.

Rausch, Robert L., "Geographic Variations in Size in North American Brown Bears, *Ursus arctos* L., as Indicated by Condylobasal Length." *Canadian Journal of Zoology,* vol. 41, 1963.

———, "On the Status of Some Arctic Mammals." *Arctic,* vol. 6, 1953.

Revere, J. W., *A Tour of Duty in California*. New York, 1849.

Roosevelt, Theodore, *Hunting Trips of a Ranchman*. New York, G. P. Putnam's Sons, 1902.

———, *The Wilderness Hunter*. New York, G. P. Putnam's Sons, 1905.

Russell, Andy, *Grizzly Country*. New York, Alfred A. Knopf, 1967.

Bibliography

————, "The People Versus the Grizzlies." *Field and Stream,* March, 1968.

Sanchez, Nellie Van De Grift, "Memoirs of a Merchant." *Touring Topics,* vol. 20, 1928.

Schrader, G. R., "The Grizzly Bear of California." Siskiyou County Historical Society, vol. 1, 1946.

Seton, Ernest Thompson, *Lives of Game Animals.* Garden City, N. Y., Doubleday, Doran and Co., 1929.

Skinner, Milton P., *Bears in the Yellowstone.* Chicago, Ill., A. C. McClurg and Co., 1925.

————, "Birth and Early Life of Grizzly Bears." *Outdoor America,* N. S., vol. 1, 1936.

Stiehm, Howard, *Game Animals of Colorado.* Colorado Game, Fish, and Parks Department, Educational Pamphlet no. 5, 1966.

Storer, Tracy I., and Lloyd P. Tevis, Jr., *California Grizzly.* Berkeley Calif., University of California Press, 1955.

Strong, W. D., "Aboriginal Society in Southern California." *University of California Publications in American Archeology and Ethnology,* vol. 26, 1929.

Sumner, Lowell, "Your Stake in Alaska's Wildlife and Wilderness." *Sierra Club Bulletin,* December, 1956.

Taylor, Robert A., Jr., "Columbia Ground Squirrel and Cambium Found in Grizzly Bear Stomachs Taken in the Fall." *Journal of Mammalogy,* vol. 45, 1964.

Tinsley, Henry G., "Grizzly Bear Lore." *Outing Magazine,* November, 1902.

Townsend, C. H., "Field Notes on Mammals, Birds and Reptiles of Northern California." *United States National Museum Proceedings,* vol. 10, 1887.

Troyer, Willard A., "The Brown Bear Harvest in Relation to Management on Kodiak Islands." *Transactions of the North American Wildlife Conference,* vol. 26, 1961.

————, and Richard J. Hensen, "Behavior of Female Brown Bears Under Stress." *Journal of Mammalogy,* vol. 45, 1964.

Umfreville, Edward, *The Present State of Hudson's Bay.* London, 1790.

Usinger, Robert L., *The Life of Rivers and Streams.* New York,

McGraw-Hill, 1967.

Van Wormer, Joe, *The World of the Black Bear*. Philadelphia, J. B. Lippincott Co., 1966.

Wagner, Henry R., *Spanish Voyages to the Northwest Coast of America in the Sixteenth Century*. San Francisco, 1929.

Ward, Rowland, *Records of Big Game*. New York, 1922.

Waters, Robert S., *Records of North American Big Game*. A book of the Boone and Crockett Club. 1964.

Wells, William, "Rocky Mountain Bears." *Forest and Stream,* January, 1899.

Whelen, Townsend, *The Kentucky Rifle*. New York, 1918.

Wright, William H., *The Grizzly Bear*. New York, Charles Scribner's Sons, 1910.

Index

Index